JOHN STEINBECK

THE GRAPES
OF WRATH

NOTES

COLES EDITORIAL BOARD

ABOUT COLES NOTES

COLES NOTES have been an indispensible aid to students on five continents since 1948.

COLES NOTES are available for a wide range of individual literary works. Clear, concise explanations and insights are provided along with interesting interpretations and evaluations.

Proper use of COLES NOTES will allow the student to pay greater attention to lectures and spend less time taking notes. This will result in a broader understanding of the work being studied and will free the student for increased participation in discussions.

COLES NOTES are an invaluable aid for review and exam preparation as well as an invitation to explore different interpretive paths.

COLES NOTES are written by experts in their fields. It should be noted that any literary judgement expressed herein is just that — the judgement of one school of thought. Interpretations that diverge from, or totally disagree with any criticism may be equally valid.

COLES NOTES are designed to supplement the text and are not intended as a substitute for reading the text itself. Use of the NOTES will serve not only to clarify the work being studied, but should enhance the reader's enjoyment of the topic.

ISBN 0 - 7740 - 3298 - 7

© COPYRIGHT 1985 AND PUBLISHED BY
COLES PUBLISHING COMPANY LIMITED
TORONTO — CANADA
PRINTED IN CANADA

CONTENTS

Steinbeck: Life and Works

John Steinbeck was born in 1902, in the town of Salinas, California. It is generally agreed that the most significant biographical link between Steinbeck and his writing is this fact of his birth and growth to maturity in the Salinas Valley. Here is the source of his knowledge and love of nature, his biological view of life (explained below), and many of his characters, whether paisanos and bums of *Tortilla Flat, Cannery Row* and *Sweet Thursday* or migrant workers of *In Dubious Battle, Of Mice and Men* and *The Grapes of Wrath*.

Steinbeck lived most of his first forty years in the Salinas Valley, where his mother taught in the public schools of the area and his father was for many years treasurer of Monterey County. (It is said that the author's early novels were written in discarded double-entry ledgers.) Steinbeck's boyhood was probably much like that of Jody in one of his most popular stories, "The Red Pony." At that time the "long valley" was a series of small farms devoted to cattle raising and the growing of fruit and vegetables, among which were interspersed little towns where the farmers brought their produce to market; young Steinbeck worked during school vacations for the neighboring farmers and ranchers. Surely these early years of life close to nature form the background from which Steinbeck draws his detailed — and often beautiful — descriptions of natural phenomena. That he attached importance to these youthful experiences in nature can be seen in the following anecdote: at the request of a publisher for early biographical facts Steinbeck replied that the most important items would probably be of little significance to others; for example, " . . . the way the sparrows hopped about on the mud street early in the morning when I was little . . . the most tremendous morning in the world when my pony had a colt."

At the same time, in addition to living close to nature as a youth, it is clear that Steinbeck read widely, probably through the influence of his schoolteacher mother. Through his fictional characters and other channels (such as correspondence) he has indicated a wide range of reading interests: Walter Scott, Jack London, Robert Louis Stevenson; Dostoyevsky's *Crime and Punishment*, Flaubert's *Madame Bovary*, Hardy's *The Return of the Native*. And it is interesting that he has commented of such reading, "certain books . . . were realer than experience. . . . I read all of these books when I was very young and I remember them not at all as books but as things that happened to me." Such remarks reveal Steinbeck's constant emphasis in his writings upon the concrete and experiential rather than the abstract and theoretical. Steinbeck has also manifested an interest in non-fictional, universally great books, such as the Bible, philosophical literature of ancient India, and Greek historians.

Although he contributed to literary publications both in high school and college (he attended Stanford University for five years as an English major, without taking a degree), the entire period of his young adulthood was intermixed with many experiences in the laboring world. Before beginning courses at Stanford he worked as an assistant chemist in a nearby sugar-beet factory. During the intervals of attendance at Stanford he was employed on ranches and road-building gangs. All of this experience provided first-hand observation of the attitudes, manners and language of the working man, as well as the foundation of his sympathy with the situation of such laborers. Even during a brief stay in New York City (1925-1927), at which point he seems to have definitely decided on a career of writing, since he made unsuccessful attempts to publish stories, he worked both as a newspaper reporter and a laborer, and he financed his return to California by shipping as a deck hand via the Panama Canal. All in all, it is clear that environment, whether the accident of his birth and growth in the Salinas Valley of California, or his own selection of various laboring jobs, figures largely in the source material of Steinbeck's writings.

It should be pointed out that Steinbeck's long residence in the Salinas Valley covered years of both regional and national unrest, changes which he observed and later utilized, especially in his three most sociologically oriented novels: *In Dubious Battle* (1936), *Of Mice and Men* (1937), and *The Grapes of Wrath* (1939). The economic structure of the Salinas Valley itself altered, as small farms were replaced by larger ones and the financial picture enlarged to include corporations, large investments and amassing fortunes. As the gap lengthened between the little man working for the big man, discontent also increased, with unemployment and threatened strikes. It was all part of the generalized national situation which culminated in the stock market crash of 1929 and the depression period following. Steinbeck's first published novel, in fact (*Cup of Gold*), appeared two months after the crash. The next few years were especially lean ones for him, as they were for many Americans, although he married, continued writing (with the help of a small subsidy and the house provided by his father), and made the acquaintance of a man who was to exert significant influence on his life for many years to come — Edward Ricketts.

A word or two should be said about Steinbeck's friendship with Ed Ricketts, the marine biologist, which lasted from their acquaintance in the 1930's until Ricketts' death in 1948. Ricketts had a commercial laboratory specializing in marine invertebrates in Pacific Grove, California. He, along with his profession, apparently elicited and guided Steinbeck's similar interests in marine biology to specific expression in a work called the *Sea of Cortez* (a record of their joint expedition to the Gulf of California), and toward the general "biological view of life" which pervades much of his writing. (Steinbeck pays special tribute to his friend in the preface to *Sea of Cortez*, in "About Ed Ricketts".) Ricketts is clearly the figure behind some of Steinbeck's most sympathetic portrayals of character (Dr. Phillips in "The Snake," Doc Burton of *In Dubious Battle*, Doc of *Cannery Row* and *Sweet Thursday*), presumably the spokesman for ideas the two men jointly held. Theirs was an intellectual relationship in which Steinbeck was able to air his views and to arrive at some of his central artistic tenets.

Steinbeck wrote prolifically and variously until his death on December 20, 1968. One of the major changes in his life, however, was his shift of residence from California to New York in 1950. (The decision is often

2

attributed in part to his deep sense of personal loss at the death of his friend Ricketts in 1948.) Significantly, a recent work, *The Winter of Our Discontent* (1961), was set in New England. Also, an account of travels throughout the United States, published in 1962 as *Travels with Charley*, seems to reflect the author's urge in the 1960's toward a revitalization of his creative powers. Steinbeck was awarded the Nobel Prize for Literature in 1962, honored, according to the official wording, for his "realistic and imaginative writings, distinguished as they are by a sympathetic humor and a social perception."

List of Major Works

Steinbeck's major works are as follows: *Cup of Gold*, 1929; *The Pastures of Heaven*, 1932; *To a God Unknown*, 1933; *Tortilla Flat*, 1935; *In Dubious Battle*, 1936; *The Red Pony*, 1937; *Of Mice and Men*, 1937; *The Long Valley*, 1938; *The Grapes of Wrath*, 1939; *Sea of Cortez*, 1941; *Bombs Away*, 1942; *The Moon Is Down*, 1942 (this work and *Of Mice and Men* also appear as plays); *Cannery Row*, 1945; *The Pearl*, 1947; *The Wayward Bus*, 1947; *East of Eden*, 1952; *Sweet Thursday*, 1954; *The Short Reign of Pippin IV*, 1957; *The Winter of Our Discontent*, 1961; *Travels with Charley*, 1962. (It should be noted that it is a second version of the Sea of Cortez expedition, published as *The Log from the Sea of Cortez*, 1951, and containing only the "Introduction" and "Narrative" from *Sea of Cortez*, which contains the memorial sketch of Ed Ricketts referred to above.)

Themes in Steinbeck's Works

Biological Theory of Man

Since certain attitudes and themes on the part of Steinbeck are commonly referred to by critics and recur in most of his writings, including *The Grapes of Wrath*, it is worthwhile to review them briefly before turning to a detailed consideration of the novel at hand. One such attitude has been referred to above as a biological view of man, developed at least in part through Steinbeck's close association with his friend, the marine biologist. Steinbeck relates human beings — his fictional characters — to plants and animals; he seems to see analogies of man in nature, in a manner not so unlike the American Transcendentalists, as represented especially by Emerson and Thoreau, who maintained a mystical reverence for all forms of natural life. His emphasis, of course, is on the natural over the supernatural; but nature in its phenomena and cycles offers even more than simple analogy, Steinbeck seems to suggest. It offers an almost spiritual comfort, and encourages an earth-founded optimism.

Philosophy of Pragmatism, or the Non-Teleological

The above term — non-teleological — is often linked with Steinbeck's biological view of man. Steinbeck himself has referred to this "philosophy" — perhaps because of his constantly refreshing urge to communicate to readers by making ideas as concrete as possible — as "is" thinking. As certain critics have explained it, "is" thinking represents "Steinbeck's own attempt to make the technical term *non-teleological* more meaningful to his readers. Broadly, what Steinbeck means is a way of thinking about life that, by concerning itself with what *is*, not with the questions of *why* or *what should be*, avoids the false judgments and exclusions of a squeamish and snobbish morality, and achieves love of life through acceptance." (E. W. Tedlock, Jr. and C. V. Wicker, *Steinbeck and his Critics*.) Such an attitude is very much in the spirit of what the famous American psychologist and philosopher, William James, termed "pragmatism," for pragmatism suggests that a man's thought and his action go hand in hand, and requires that men reason about and judge events as they are experiencing them, instead of applying facilely to their experiences preconceived "why's" and "what should be's." "Is" thinking, or pragmatic thinking, then, recognizes that theoretical or abstract thought does not always fit reality, the way life really happens. To form such a way of thinking into a kind of philosophy, as Steinbeck seems to do, is to express one's belief in a human world of realizable goals, rather than a dream world of impossible ideals.

Steinbeck's Social Consciousness

Although it is perhaps unfortunate for Steinbeck's total literary reputation that the first three of his novels which received serious critical attention were sociologically oriented (since this has caused many critics to read social criticism forcibly into all his works), it is nevertheless certainly true that social consciousness represents a basic element in his writings. This is especially true for *In Dubious Battle* (1936), *Of Mice and Men* (1937), and *The Grapes of Wrath* (1939), all of which were post-depression novels, and dealt with proletarian matter. The first-mentioned novel is concerned with specific social problems of the period — violence, particularly of strikes and strike-breaking, and the ineffectuality of both "left" and "right," politically speaking, in bringing about more humane conditions and equitable solutions to labor conflicts. The second novel is more involved with men — little men — and their struggles than with generalized social problems. Of this story, about a feeble-minded character, Lennie, and his friend, George, who dream of owning a farm in California, Steinbeck wrote that he was dealing with "the earth longings of a Lennie who was not to represent insanity at all but the inarticulate and powerful yearning of all men." At another time he declared that *Of Mice and Men* was "a study of the dreams and pleasures of everyone in the world," an indication of the continuing emphasis in his writings on individual man and his strivings rather than stark social criticism. *The Grapes of Wrath*, to be treated below, is, of course, his epic masterpiece of social consciousness in its picture of helpless people crushed by drought and depression. Even here, though, as in all his works to follow, Steinbeck's focus is upon man; the nature of man and his success and failures, rather than upon the mere detached picture of an indifferent society. (In contrast, for example, to some of Steinbeck's immediate forerunners in American fiction, such as

Frank Norris and Theodore Dreiser, who depicted man simply as a wisp in the wind of giant American industrialism and stampeding capitalism.)

Dream and Reality, A Fantasy World

There is an element in Steinbeck's fiction which belongs more to a fantasy or dream world than it does to the real everyday world. Sometimes this element manifests itself in the author's choice of protagonists from among the feeble-minded, the castoffs of society and the antisocial; in other instances it is seen in his descriptions, which often open chapters, and conjure up a dream-like atmosphere (this descriptive quality is especially evident in *Tortilla Flat, Cannery Row and Sweet Thursday*). Steinbeck's choice of central characters, in particular, has caused much controversy among critics as to his intentions and the successful realization of them. He has been accused of "glorifying idiocy," (for example, in Lennie, *Of Mice and Men*), or of "deifying the drunk, canonizing the castoff" — the major figures in *Cannery Row,* for instance, by his own stipulation, are society's "no-goods and blots-on-the-town and bums." Similarly, Danny and his friends (in *Tortilla Flat*) live, what by ordinary standards is certainly an unreal existence, surviving more through chance than by planning, and "experiencing" life in a most random way. Or, the characters in *The Wayward Bus* seem selected by the author more for some separate point he wishes to probe about each of them than for the likelihood that they could have, in reality, been thrust together for the rambling bus ride.

We have seen that of Lennie, the halfwit (*Of Mice and Men*), Steinbeck stated he was to represent "the inarticulate and powerful yearning of all men . . . the dreams and pleasures of everyone in the world." It is likewise clear from Steinbeck's numerous statements on the book, *Tortilla Flat*, which is episodic (that is, it seems to be a series of episodes strung together, often by dreamlike descriptions), that he intended it to be a kind of modern Arthurian cycle, a story of 20th century knights of the Round Table, although related in a mock-epic or humorous tone. (The author has spoken, for example, as late as 1957 — *Tortilla Flat* is dated 1935 — of his continuing interest in Sir Thomas Malory's *Le Morte d'Arthur,* and his desire to travel to England to study the manuscript and discuss it with an Arthurian scholar.) Similar objectives outside realistic narrative, along the lines of allegorical symbolic meanings, can be detected in, say, *The Wayward Bus,* which Steinbeck concludes with an epigraph quoting from a well-known medieval "morality" play called *Everyman*, a drama which chronicled (somewhat like the familiar *Pilgrim's Progress* of John Bunyan) the cycle of *every man's* life from birth to death. These few examples indicate that, however critics may judge his efforts, or however his goals are actually realized, in much of his work Steinbeck is striving beyond realistic narrative or mere social protest, attempting to chronicle, in near-epic form, the struggles of individual men. Those critics who have come especially close to Steinbeck's work in all its stages (for example, Peter Lisca, E. W. Tedlock, Jr., C. V. Wicker, Warren French)

5

attest to the comprehensiveness and complexity of his plan and approach for each novel.

General Introduction to
The Grapes of Wrath

The Grapes of Wrath is usually described as a novel of social protest, for it exposes the desperate conditions under which one group of American workers, the migratory farm families, was forced to live during the 1930's. These were the people who, in the depths of the greatest economic depression the United States has known, had to abandon their homes and their livelihoods. They were uprooted and set adrift because tractors were rapidly industrializing the Southern cotton fields and because erosion and drought were creating the Dust Bowl in wide areas of Kansas, Colorado, New Mexico, Texas, and Oklahoma.

Many of these families moved only short distances; but over one hundred and fifty thousand others migrated to California, Steinbeck's home, where their presence caused acute social stresses. Although the migrants were eager to obtain work, many landed proprietors took advantage of their poverty and distress by hiring them at starvation wages, treating them with great brutality, and denying them even the most elementary human and civil rights. Indeed, as part of their program of exploitation, the landowners tried to suppress all attempts at organization by the migrant workers — who were contemptuously referred to as "Okies" — and it was not until 1937, at the earliest, that some of them were able to form a union for self-protection. Even then, the union grew slowly; but it did hold promise of an eventual improvement in working conditions — a promise that remained unfulfilled, ironically, until World War II began to draw thousands of Americans into national defence plants.

Such, in brief were the contemporary events upon which Steinbeck based his most famous novel, and he reported them accurately, realistically, and sympathetically. He had, of course, explored contemporary social problems in earlier works such as *In Dubious Battle* and *Of Mice and Men,* but here he found a theme of greater scope and passion. The idea for *The Grapes of Wrath* undoubtedly grew out of a series of articles on California's migrant labor camps, which Steinbeck had been commissioned to write for the San Francisco *News*. He later gained first-hand knowledge by living in migrant camps and by travelling Route 66 between Oklahoma and California.

These experiences may help to explain the power which Steinbeck displays in *The Grapes of Wrath,* both in the epic scope of his narrative and the deep sympathy with which he treats the misery, suffering, and degradation of the Joad family during their long journey from the exhausted Dust Bowl to the fertile valleys of California. Yet the bitterness and anger he feels is equally strong, for Steinbeck makes it clear that the plight of the Joad family and of thousands of other families was, in his view, a man-made evil and that, as a man-made evil, it could be remedied by man. The simple urgency of his message, therefore, has caused *The Grapes of Wrath* — the title comes from Julia Ward Howe's "The Battle Hymn of the Republic" — to be compared to *Uncle Tom's Cabin* on the grounds that it was as much a propagandistic tract for its time as the other had been for an earlier period. And both works were, in turn, as bitterly attacked as they were popular and influential.

Of all the social novels that came out of the great depression — and there were many such novels of protest — very few have condemned man's inhumanity to man with the persistence, forcefulness, and intermittent vividness Steinbeck's epic work displays. The 1930's comprised a decade of crisis, moral as well as economic, in which the initial financial panic was followed first by depression and then by paralysis. Under these conditions, only a vast social revolution — of which the New Deal of Franklin D. Roosevelt's administration became the principal agency — seemed to hold any hope of restoring faith in the democratic processes, whether economic or social.

In response to the national crisis, American novelists returned, by and large, to naturalism as the mode of literary composition best fitted to evoke their new sense of reality — the pervasive fear, despair, and hopelessness that followed the apparent collapse of the economic and political structure of American society. Everywhere he looked, the American writer of the 1930's seemed to see only hunger and unemployment, desperate struggle and brutal expression, and it appeared to him an ugly world in which the individual, especially the victim of the depression, the man on relief, was at the mercy of forces, both social and economic, he could neither understand nor control.

Such a deterministic view of life is to be found, if indirectly, in *The Grapes of Wrath*, and it is at the very heart of the philosophy of naturalism. That philosophy had its origins in nineteenth century scientific thought, particularly in the theories of Charles Darwin, and its most notable literary exponent, from the American viewpoint, was Emile Zola. Zola often placed his characters in certain environments, as though they were undergoing a controlled scientific experiment, in order to study their responses and behavior, and his scientific fiction had a strong influence, at the turn of the last century, upon the novels of Frank Norris, Jack London, and Upton Sinclair (all three of whom were, like Steinbeck, Californians and set some of their stories in that state). There have been, of course, other practitioners of naturalism since, most notably Theodore Dreiser; but it was not until the depression years that naturalism underwent a sharp revival in the work of such writers as James Farrell, Erskine Caldwell and Richard Wright.

In general, naturalism takes the form of a study of the gradual degeneration of a man under the impact of his heredity or environment. The classic examples of naturalism examine that degeneration from either a biological point of view, which derives from Darwin, or from an economic point of view, which derives from Karl Marx. There are, to be sure, many deviations from the classic types: some novels, especially the American novels of the 1930's, contain both points of view. Others, often referred to more generally as novels of social protest or as proletarian novels, may be neither militantly, nor perhaps even consciously, Darwinian or Marxist in their points of view.

What all these naturalistic novels have in common, though, is their pessimism: the philosophy of naturalism does not sustain the belief that the individual can govern or control his own fate.

In the 1930's, the emphasis of naturalism was shifting from the individual to the group, but the deterministic view remained firm. The naturalistic novel of the 1930's described the struggles of various minority groups — the Irish, Negroes, workers, Okies — and it attempted to become socially significant by employing the techniques of shock. Since the announced intention of this literary movement was to portray life as it really was, as the great social disaster of the early 1930's had clearly shown it to be, then the writer's very fidelity to the ugliness and brutality of life might well shock people, he believed, into taking direct action to alleviate misery, remove inequities, and help create a new society in which all might share.

But however much of a naturalist Steinbeck was in his rebellion against social oppression and injustice, he did not slip into the mechanically violent and perhaps over-simplified view of life that many naturalists tended to embrace. Like the naturalists, who often saw the bestial in man breaking through his veneer of civilized behavior, especially at moments of tension and excitement, Steinbeck emphasizes the close relationship between animal and human nature and shows a great interest in what critics have called the biology of human affairs. But, unlike the naturalists of his own period, Steinbeck sees more than simply the oppression and degeneration of the unfortunates he portrays; he does not permit his characters to succumb completely, to become mere pawns of their environment and their dark fate. Despite all their suffering, the Joads, in *The Grapes of Wrath*, exhibit a deep, instinctive will to survive, animal in its stubbornness, elemental in its forcefulness, and primitive in its dignity. It is a stubbornness that seems destined not merely to help them endure but to make them prevail; for such people as these, Steinbeck seems to say, shall indeed inherit the earth, and they shall inherit the earth simply because they remain loyal to life itself.

This quality in Steinbeck's best work is not usually articulated very clearly, and we would have to turn to the work of William Faulkner to find it realized. In Steinbeck, the will to survive exists in simple opposition to the pessimistic determinism that also seems to fascinate him, but then it evokes his most poetic prose, flashes of joy and mystic communication, and, indeed, a note of hope. Such a humanistic sympathy and tenderness is not to be found in other novels of the period — as a general rule, that is, since William Faulkner is the notable exception. For in order to evoke sympathy for the sufferings of his characters, the purely naturalistic writer often inverts his tenderness into the desire to shock and brutalize. Steinbeck, however, does not go to such extremes and does not distort so much, and it is precisely the sense of promise, of possibility, muted, diffused, and intermittent as it may be, that lifts *The Grapes of Wrath* from the comparatively narrow strictures of the naturalistic novel into the broader realms of the romance. And in so doing, it links Steinbeck's romance-novel to a large movement in American literature — the search for the fulfilment of the American dream.

Such a quest has often taken the form of a journey westward — away, that is, from society to a new and freer way of life, perhaps even to a promised land. Our forefathers had, of course, come westward to the New World in search of a new way of life, and their descendants had gradually extended the frontier westward against all obstacles and difficulties. Steinbeck, too, has long been concerned with the westward trek: Joseph Wayne, in *To a God Unknown*, and Adam Trask, in *East of Eden*, both leave their New England homes for the valleys of California; so too, though from Oklahoma, the Joads, dispossessed by drought and depression, start westward — but they start westward not only to seek work and a home but peace and hope. In short, now that their old world has been destroyed, they journey westward to seek a new life in a new world, the world they — like so many Americans before them — have dreamed of but never fully realized. In this sense, then, *The Grapes of Wrath*, although a naturalistic novel protesting social and economic injustice, is also symbolic of a greater search within the hearts and minds of those who are making the journey, who have left one world but have not yet reached the other. The frontier had once been a physical one; by the 1930's it had become an economic one, yet the Joad family's journey, as the presence of the former preacher, Jim Casy, implies, becomes symbolic of both the material and spiritual energies that have long been engaged in discovering, conquering, and settling a still undiscovered continent, a natural and moral paradise, perhaps even an Eden.

Such, at least, seems to be the prevailing critical view, and those who support it point out that the journey from an old world to a new one, the theme of withdrawal and return, has had a long history in American life and literature. Thoreau and Melville, to name but two, withdrew from society, the one to Walden Pond, the other to the South Seas, in order to meditate. James Fenimore Cooper's Natty Bumppo and Mark Twain's Huckleberry Finn are but two fictional characters who either withdrew from, or rebelled against, society and then made long journeys in search of a dream or an ideal that society itself had not yet realized. So, too, in an important sense, with Steinbeck's Joad family, which withdrew, as it were, from the old world to create a new one and then attempted, despite man's inhumanity to man, to return to society, to rediscover and reassert their sense of human solidarity and unity. In the attempt, Steinbeck is following in a native tradition that assumes the proportions of myth.

The Grapes of Wrath is a strongly sustained social and political narrative that provides an accurate and faithful description of a critical period in American history. It recreates in painful detail a decade of despair and suffering, of social instability and experimentation. As a work of fiction, it attempts to transcend the purely documentary, the materials of which may have seemed to result only in hopelessness and negation, by incorporating into the novel several of the attributes of the romance — most notably, the impulse toward the mythic and symbolic — in order to achieve universal human significance and to say something hopeful about human nature.

Characters in the Novel

AL and MAE   Proprietors of a small hamburger stand on Highway 66.

BLACK HAT   A disgruntled migrant worker in the government camp at Weedpatch, California. He speculates on the possibility of the migrants organizing against the California landowners.

BULLITT, JESSIE (MRS.)   The chairman of the Welcoming Committee at Weedpatch, the government camp.

CASY, JIM   Casy is a former itinerant preacher. He accompanies the Joads to California.

DAVIS   The driver of the tractor which plows through the Oklahoma tenant-farmers' land and knocks over their houses.

EATON, WILLIE   The tough Texan who is chairman of the Entertainment Committee for the Weedpatch camp dance.

FEELEY, WILLY   A deputy sheriff who, according to Muley Graves, is persecuting him.

GRAVES, MULEY   The Oklahoma farmer whose property was near the Joads' farm and who obstinately refuses to be driven off his land by dust, tractors, or deputies.

HUSTON, EZRA   The elected chairman of Weedpatch camp's Central Committee.

JACKSON   Supposedly a friend of the three young men who try to cause trouble at the Weedpatch camp dance.

JOAD, AL   The sixteen-year-old son who is interested only in cars and girls.

JOAD, GRAMPA   The honorary head of the Joad family. He originally settled the 40 acres which Pa Joad lost.

JOAD, GRANMA   Grampa's obstinate, fiercely religious wife.

JOAD, UNCLE JOHN   Pa Joad's fifty-year-old brother.

JOAD, MA   The strong, determined wife and mother who controls the family and holds it together.

JOAD, NOAH   The oldest son who is slightly deformed and quietly strange.

JOAD, PA   A tenant farmer who has lost his farm to the crop destroying dust storms of Oklahoma. He is taking his family to California where he hopes to find work.

JOAD, RUTHIE AND WINFIELD   The two youngest members of the Joad family. Ruthie is twelve, Winfield ten.

JOAD, TOM   The elder son who is on parole from the state prison, where he served four years for manslaughter.

JOE   The labor contractor who comes to the Hooverville looking for men to pick fruit in Tulare County.

JOYCE, MRS.   A timid woman at the Weedpatch camp whose daughters have been sick.

KNOWLES, FLOYD   A young husband and father at the Hooverville outside Bakersfield. He strikes a deputy and Casy takes all the blame.

LITTLEFIELD, ANNIE   One of the members of the Weedpatch camp Welcoming Committee.

MAE   Mae and Al run a hamburger stand on Highway 66.

MIKE   The fat deputy who comes to the aid of Joe, the Tulare labor contractor. Mike tries to arrest Floyd Knowles, who strikes him and runs away.

RAWLEY, JIM   The camp manager at Weedpatch.

RIVERS, CONNIE   Rose of Sharon's nineteen-year-old husband.

RIVERS, ROSE OF SHARON JOAD   Rose of Sharon is the older of the two Joad daughters. She is married to Connie Rivers, and is pregnant when the trek west begins.

SANDRY, LISBETH   A religious fanatic at the Weedpatch camp.

SUMMERS, ELLA   One of the members of the Weedpatch camp Welcoming Committee.

THOMAS, MR.   The small rancher near Weedpatch government camp. Timothy Wallace, his son Wilkie, and Tom Joad work a few days laying pipe for Mr. Thomas.

VITELA, JULE   A half-Cherokee Indian at the Weedpatch camp. Jule and Tom are posted at the gate before the dance begins, to keep out any possible trouble-makers.

WAINWRIGHT, AGGIE   The fifteen-year-old girl whom Al intends to marry. The Wainwrights share a boxcar with the Joads in the cotton area near Tulare.

WAINWRIGHT, MR. & MRS.   Wainwright, his wife and daughter Aggie share a boxcar with the Joads near Tulare.

WALLACE, TIMOTHY   A Weedpatch resident who tells Tom Joad about the pipe-laying job at Mr. Thomas' ranch.

WALLACE, WILKIE   Mr. Wallace's son who works with his father and Tom Joad on the pipe-laying job.

WALLACE, MRS. WILKIE   The young mother in the Wallace tent at Weedpatch who is presumably married to Wilkie Wallace.

WILSON, IVY   The owner of the stalled Dodge which the Joads spot just beyond Oklahoma city. The Joads camp beside them, the two families become friends, and they continue the trip west together after Al and Tom repair the Dodge.

WILSON, SAIRY   Sairy and her husband Ivy Wilson are trying to travel from Kansas to California in an antiquated Dodge. When the Joads and Wilsons reach the California border, Sairy is too sick to proceed.

Plot Summary

As the story begins, Tom Joad, a young man of about thirty, is hitch-hiking home to his parents' farm in Oklahoma. He is dressed in cheap new clothes, for he has just been released from prison, on parole, after serving four years of a seven years' sentence for homicide. During a drunken brawl at a community dance, Tom, in retaliation for being knifed, had killed his assail-ant with a blow from a shovel. Not far from his destination, however, he is forced to rest in the shade of a willow tree; the heat is intense, the drought fierce, and thick dust powders the wilting corn and spurts up beneath his feet. There he meets a man who remembers him as a boy, who had, in fact, baptized him. Jim Casy, for years a preacher, has left his vocation, he tells Tom, because he has had grave misgivings about his motives and because, during the time he has been thinking things over, he has become convinced that all men have one great soul of which each individual has a small bit for himself.

Casy accompanies Tom to his parents' farm, but when the two men reach the Joad place they find it deserted, the house falling down and cotton planted in the dooryard. From a neighbor, Muley Graves, they learn that Tom's family is temporarily boarding at his Uncle John's farm, from which he too is being evicted, and that they are all planning to migrate westward to find a new home and a new livelihood. The drought has become worse, the crops are failing, and the banks are not only evicting families from their farms but bringing in tractors that can do the work of fifteen families apiece.

Muley is determined to stay on the land, even though his family has already gone westward. But he is alone in his determination; even Casy decides to join the migrants, if Tom's family will accept him. At Uncle John's, Tom receives a warm welcome from his parents and his five brothers and sisters; they have nearly finished packing for the long trip, selling at a loss whatever they cannot carry with them, and slaughtering the pigs and salting down the meat to use as food en route. They have one hundred and fifty-four dollars to support twelve people — thirteen now that they have taken Casy in — on a journey across half a continent, and the old Hudson automobile in which they will travel will soon need new tires.

Although the Joads have to drug Grampa to make him go — he suddenly refused to budge — they are all soon driving westward along Highway 66, which will take them across Oklahoma, the Texas Panhandle, New Mexico, Arizona, and into California. But even before they have left the state of Oklahoma, troubles begin: one of their dogs is hit and killed by an automobile on the highway; a filling station operator is suspicious of helping them until he knows they have money; and Grampa, who has become sicker, suddenly dies of a stroke — as if he could not bear to leave the land in which he had so long been rooted. By this time, however, the Joads have made friends with the Wilsons, a couple who help them during Grampa's last illness and burial in a nearby field, and the two families decide to travel together in their two vehicles, sharing alike. Folks need to help each other, as Mrs. Wilson says, and that Ma Joad agrees soon becomes evident. For when one of the automobiles breaks down and Tom suggests that they split up for the rest of the journey, Ma rebels against her own husband and sons, refuses to permit the family to break up, and, in effect, takes over the leadership of the family from Pa Joad, her husband.

As they approach California, however — weary, undernourished, and increasingly desperate — the difficulties seem to multiply. There are proprietors who charge the migrants for a place to camp overnight because they know the police will arrest those who camp along the highways. There is the ragged man on his way back from California who tells the Joads that the handbills they have seen offering employment in California are, at the best, misleading. And there is the Texan who tells them, soon after they have entered California, what it is like to be called an "Okie" — a gesture of contempt, he indicates, on the part of people who are so scared themselves that they must hate all strangers. Noah Joad, the eldest, leaves the family by simply wading down the river by which they have temporarily camped. Granma has become ill, and she talks to Grampa as if he were still alive. A sheriff comes by to warn Ma that she and her family had better be gone by daybreak. While crossing the desert, however, Granma dies — just before they catch their first glimpse of the green valleys of California; and although the Joads have but forty dollars left, they are determined to bury her properly.

They are in California at last, at the end of their journey, and now the search for employment begins. Their first step is Hooverville in which there are forty tents and shacks, an automobile parked by each one. They soon learn that these so-called Hoovervilles spring up wherever migrants gather to camp for a night or for several nights in their search for employment. From Floyd Knowles, a young man with whom Tom and Al Joad strike up a friendship, the Joads learn about the enormous numbers of unemployed and starving migrants, the vicious tactics used against them by the landowners, and the hopelessness of attempting to organize a rebellion.

When a contractor shows up at the camp to offer temporary employment picking fruit, Floyd is accused of talking like a Communist agitator simply because he tries to make the contractor specify both the rate of pay and the number of men required for the job. On this charge, then, Floyd is to be taken into custody, but as the deputy takes him by the arm, Floyd hits him and Tom trips him. The deputy nevertheless continues to fire at the fleeing Floyd, and Casy kicks him unconscious. Since Tom is sure to be in deep trouble — he has broken parole by leaving the state of Oklahoma — Casy takes upon himself the full responsibility for the incident and gives himself up to the reinforcements that soon arrive. The Joads, of course, must leave — even though Connie Rivers has deserted his wife, Rose of Sharon, the Joads' eldest daughter, who has been pregnant throughout the long journey, and even though Uncle John is on one of his drunken sprees.

A comparatively idyllic interlude ensues at a government camp, where the children learn the marvels of modern plumbing and the adults the procedures of democratic self-government. Food runs low, though, and Ma insists that they must move on to find work. This time they appear to be lucky, for they are employed to pick peaches at five cents a box. There is something ominous about the ease with which they find work: the seven Joads, including the two children, Ruthie and Winfield, are able to earn one dollar for a full afternoon's work — money which is promptly spent, however, at the food store run by the owners of the farm, where prices are higher than in town. Then, as if to confirm their suspicions, they discover that they are under surveillance by armed guards. When Tom succeeds in slipping by the guards one night, he encounters an old friend outside, Jim Casy, now a labor organizer. He is, in fact, leading a strike against the owners of this very farm because they were paying but two and a half cents a box — that is, a dollar for each *ton* of peaches picked by hand. While Tom and Casy are talking, a strike-breaker comes upon them in the dark, recognizes Casy in the beams of his flashlight, and kills him with a blow of a pick handle.

In retaliation, Tom kills Casy's murderer, and then manages to sneak back to their cabin undetected. He is fully aware that he is now an outlaw who will be hunted down by the owners and the police. Ma refuses, however, to let him leave the family. When prices drop back to two and a half cents, the Joads depart in their automobile, keeping Tom well hidden beneath mattresses. Although they soon find another temporary job, picking cotton while living in nearby boxcars, Tom has to remain hidden in a culvert, to which Ma brings food after dark. Unfortunately, Ruthie, their twelve year old daughter, betrays Tom's secret to other children, and then Ma has no choice but to tell her son that he must, for his own safety, leave them. Al Joad, too, has been talking about leaving the family; but since he wishes to marry Aggie Wainwright, daughter of the family sharing their boxcar, he does not do so immediately.

Rose of Sharon, however, is nearing her time; and as the rains begin to fall, as the floods begin to rise about the boxcars, she gives birth to her child, who is born dead. And on the third day of the rains, the Joads are forced to abandon their shelter, to seek refuge on higher ground, and there, in a barn occupied only by a boy and his starving father, the Joads find shelter once again. There, after she has looked deep into the eyes of her mother, Rose of Sharon cradles the starving old man in her arms and offers him her breast from which to suck.

Characterization

Such, in brief, is the narrative from which emerges what we usually call the process of characterization. Characterization is, finally, inseparable from the action of the story itself, indeed from the very language itself, yet neither the narrative summarized above nor the characterization of the Joads either as individuals or as a family unit can be separated from the dozen or more generalized chapters that are scattered throughout *The Grapes of Wrath*. These are commonly referred to as intercalary, or interchapters, for they are very short and take up about one-sixth of the novel. The Joads appear in none of the interchapters, which are intended to provide the physical, social, political, and historical setting and background for the action of the story itself — and, ultimately, for the characterization of those involved in the story.

These short chapters take up a variety of subjects. Some, for example, provide the social and economic background, such as the dialogue in Chapter V between owners and tenants, which is really a generalized dialogue between the representatives of industrial and agrarian ideals, the bankers, and farmers. It follows upon Tom's first glimpse of his parents' abandoned farm. Some give the historical background, such as Chapter XIX, which summarizes the history of the ownership of land in the state of California. It follows right upon the Joads' first glimpse of the green valleys of California after they have crossed the desert. Some are, in effect, political and philosophical, such as Chapter XIV, where the author himself seems to be offering a little sermon on the confusion between causes and results, on the need to develop from the individual, selfish "I" to the communal, unselfish "we," and on his essentially optimistic view that for every step forward taken by mankind there is, at the worst, only half a step backward. The latter view is echoed, in the main narrative, by Jim Casy, just before he is murdered, and it indicates that many of the general themes and subjects found in the interchapters are to be enunciated or embodied by the characters of the main narrative itself. There are also some interchapters that serve to generalize the immediately preceding incident. For example, Chapter IX, which describes the evicted tenants selling their household belongings, follows right upon Al Joad's driving into Sallisaw with a load of furniture the Joads are forced to sell.

Whatever the variations, then, the intention is clear — to interweave, interlock, or juxtapose the particular and the general; that is, to relate the specific actions of the Joads to similar actions of thousands of other families who were as deeply shattered by drought and depression during the grim 1930's. Evidently, Steinbeck wished not only to generalize the particular experiences of the Joads, to link the personal and the familiar to the communal and, indeed, the national, but to universalize that experience in so doing. The first and final interchapters provide the framework for the novel, the two poles, so to speak, between which the action of the novel discharges itself. In the opening chapter, the coming of summer to Oklahoma is described: the sun scorches the land, the corn wilts, the dust rises, and the women anxiously watch the faces of their men to see if anger will break through the perplexity and fear. The theme of anger, the burgeoning and ripening of the grapes of wrath, continues to underlie the long journey of the Joads — Ma herself, at one point, tells Tom that when she can make his father mad, she knows he's all right — and, finally, it reasserts itself in the final interchapter: as the rains begin to fall in California, the women again anxiously watch the faces of their men.

So the particular is framed, as it were, between two general instances, one of drought and one of flood. Yet the second interchapter has, in the meantime, introduced a turtle, one of the oldest forms of animal life still surviving in the world, and it is evidently intended to tell us something about the Joads. For the turtle struggles heroically to climb the high embankment along the highway, mounts the concrete slab with difficulty, and then narrowly escapes the wheels of two automobiles, one of which, attempting to crush it, succeeds only in flipping it off the road. In the meantime, the turtle has inadvertently crushed an ant that ran inside its shell and carried across the highway a head of wild oats, which then falls out and roots itself. The turtle, in turn, is picked up by Tom Joad as he crosses the highway on his way to his parents' farm, then is rolled up with Tom's shoes in his coat as a present for the youngsters, and finally is released at the Joads' abandoned farm. This series of events, as many critics have observed, is to be interpreted allegorically, for the Joads will display the same determination in the face of obstacles; they will refuse to be deflected from their goals, and they will survive and endure. Ma Joad is the most obvious embodiment of the turtle's stubborn determination, but of course she, in turn, is being generalized into all women who suffer and endure for the sakes of their families. She symbolizes the principle of continuity.

If, then, the turtle seems to suggest the qualities of character needed to survive a long and difficult journey — and hence to show the correlation between action and character — it might be well to remark briefly upon other possible allegorical or symbolic relationships. The very title of the book, as well as the varied references both to grapes of wrath and to grapes of plenty, has led several critics back to the Bible; there they have found parallels between the Israelites' exodus from Egypt to Canaan and the journey of the Joads from Oklahoma to California. Since Rose of Sharon is also of Biblical derivation, they have suggested that perhaps Steinbeck intended Rose of Sharon's final act to be understood as miraculous. For it is indeed from the very depths of despair, at the end of a long journey from drought to flood, from one natural disaster to another, that Rose of Sharon offers her full breast to a starving old man — a natural and symbolic act in the service of life, amid a flood. Then, too, Tom Joad and Jim Casy, as these critics note — they point to the initials J.C. — are converted, as it were, during the course of their journey, from selfishness to unselfishness, from a desire to gratify themselves to a need to help others, to improve the lot of all who suffer and are heavy laden. Casy dies for his new beliefs, a martyr to a cause, and Tom, his disciple, is forced to become an outlaw, a refugee from justice; but both men display according to this critical view, certain Biblical and indeed Christian attributes.

It would be a mistake, however, to press for any consistency of religious interpretation, whether allegorical or symbolic, on the basis of a few, random instances, for the materials of the novel simply will not support it. Steinbeck has provided only the form, the shell, as it were, from which the original content has been emptied; he has not achieved the fusion of form and content, the unity of meaning which is the first condition for more complex interpretations. But that may be a way of saying that Steinbeck is really concerned with the archetypal and mythic — that is, with the search, in a specifically American setting, for a natural and moral paradise by a family that assumes heroic proportions. From this point of view, a Biblical theme remains implicit; but it has become, in the best American tradition, more and more secularized. The novel becomes more secularized, however, without losing either the vaguely spiritual implications or the native optimism inherent, for example, in Rose of Sharon's final gesture of faith.

More illuminating, though, might be Tom's first talk with Jim Casy. Even before he has reached his parents' farm, Tom listens to Casy speak of his withdrawal from preaching, of what he has learned during his self-searching, and of his vague need to apply the lessons he has learned. He specifically tells Tom that he has begun to recognize how inseparable the Holy Spirit and the human spirit really are and how the soul of each individual is but one small part of the big soul that is everybody. It is a lesson that Tom comes to accept for himself; at the end of the novel, as he is parting from his mother, he speaks of Casy's philosophy: since each individual has a small share in one great soul, he tells her, it doesn't really matter whether or not he is killed, as she fears he may be, because he will always be near her, near anyone who is in trouble. Ma Joad has, in her own way, said much the same thing, for she once told Tom that they were the people, the people who live and continue, and Steinbeck himself, as we mentioned earlier, spoke of the need for the maturation of the "I" into the "we" — a need that may be said to control the whole intention of the novel. The important point, however, is that such philosophizing is but another means of characterization. It may be called the philosophical or spiritual counterpart of the biological unity symbolized by the turtle.

Chapter Summaries and Commentaries

CHAPTER 1

Summary

The last rain fell on the red and grey country of Oklahoma in early May. The weeds became a dark green to protect themselves from the sun's unyielding rays. The corn faded and dried, and a layer of crust formed over the earth. In June, the sun shone more fiercely and the earth paled with each passing day. A few raindrops fell, but only enough to spot the land. The wind grew stronger, uprooting the weakened corn, and the air became so filled with dust that the stars were not visible at night.

When morning came and the wind had ceased, the men came out of their homes and looked upon the ruined corn as it lay dying in the hot sun. The women stood beside their men to sense whether their spirit had been broken. "Women and children knew deep in themselves that no misfortune was too great to bear if their men were whole."

Commentary

The opening chapter paints a vivid picture of the situation facing the drought-stricken farmers of Oklahoma. The drought, which has turned the earth to dust and ruined the crops, will lead to the great migration to California.

A distinctive feature throughout the novel is the idleness of the men and the way in which the women watch them for signs of breaking. The women feel that they can bear anything, as long as their men remain "whole" and unbroken.

The first chapter is one of several chapters interspersed throughout the novel that are of general importance. These intercalary, or interchapters, usually follow a chapter of narration and are designed to put the plight of the Joads in perspective, both nationally and historically.

CHAPTER 2

Summary

In Chapter 1 Steinbeck gives the reader a general picture of the ruinous conditions faced by the Oklahoma sharecropper. Now he introduces us to a particular member of a particular family, Tom Joad. Following the misfortunes of the Joad family, Steinbeck will, throughout the novel, switch back and forth from the trials of this one family to the more generic problems faced by the society of which the Joad family is but one unit.

Tom Joad has been in prison four years for killing a man in a drunken brawl. He is walking back home and, seeing a transport truck beside a roadside restaurant, he decides to hitch a ride. The driver points out that there is a NO RIDERS sticker on the windshield, but Tom observes that "sometimes a guy'll be a good guy even if some rich bastard makes him carry a sticker." The truck driver, wanting to be a "good guy" and wishing to prove that he does not fear his employer, succumbs to Tom's shrewdly worded request. As soon as the truck has rounded the corner and is out of sight of the restaurant, he picks up Tom.

The driver, who prides himself on his powers of observation, begins to ask Tom about himself. He is surprised to learn that Tom's father is a forty acre sharecropper who has not yet been "dusted out" or "tractored out." Tom becomes annoyed at the driver's attempts to guess his identity and volunteers to provide him with any information he might want. Aware that he has been too inquisitive, the driver tries to justify his interest by telling Tom he enjoys noticing little things because it helps to pass the time. Realizing the driver has probably already guessed he is an ex-convict, Tom decides to satisfy his curiosity and give him something to talk about "in every joint from here to Texola." He admits that he has just finished serving four years of a seven-year sentence for homicide. For the benefit of the nosy driver, Tom emphasizes, "I'm sprung in four for keepin' my nose clean." As the truck roars off, Tom turns into the dusty road to his father's house.

Commentary

The driver is suprised to learn that Tom's father is a forty acre sharecropper who has not been "dusted out" or "tractored out." These terms require some explanation. The sharecropper did not own the land, but was merely a tenant farmer. He was allowed to keep a share of the crop while the remainder went to pay taxes and the bank or the finance company which owned the land. Now that Oklahoma has been turned into a dust bowl, sharecroppers are in debt and the owners wish to repossess the land. By planting cotton fast, paying one man to run a huge tractor over the smaller holdings and thus turn them into one large farm, the owners can still make a profit for a few more years before the land is completely dead. Thus the sharecroppers are to be "tractored out," and anyone who refuses to leave peacefully will have his home ripped out from under him.

In this chapter the basic conflict between the haves and the have-nots is introduced when Tom suggests that the have-nots, like himself and the truck driver, ought to stick together against the rich.

CHAPTER 3

Summary

The concrete highway is edged with dry grass and clover and weeds. And each of these plants, though seemingly dead, is actually teeming with sleeping life. Each has an abundance of seeds waiting for the chance passing of an animal, the wind, or perhaps a human to dislodge them and spread them over a great area.

Through this sea of sleeping life moves an army of insects and one lone land turtle — "turning aside for nothing, dragging his high-domed shell over the grass." The turtle leaves a little trail behind him strewn with the seed he has shaken loose.

By a prodigious effort the turtle manages to climb up the road embankment. But once on the hot pavement there are other hazards. A sedan driven by a woman swerves around the turtle, but a man driving a light truck deliberately hits the animal, flipping it over and rolling it off the highway. After a long time the turtle rights itself and continues in its former direction.

Commentary

This short, intercalary chapter is important for several reasons. First of all, it provides us with a brilliant example of Steinbeck's realism. The turtle and other forms of life are described not only with artistry, but also with scientific accuracy. Next, we have in this passage an implicit expression of Steinbeck's naturalistic philosophy: the turtle is determined to persevere and, in the process, he relentlessly crushes opposing ants and sows seeds of future vegetative life. Also, the migration of the turtle prefigures the migration of the Okies in general and the Joads in particular. Finally, it might be argued that the seemingly gratuitous details of the truck driver and the woman driver may suggest Steinbeck's awareness that men often tend to be destructive whereas women are generally more protective: Tom Joad has committed manslaughter while Ma Joad and Rose of Sharon, as we shall see later, are continually trying to preserve the family and nurture life.

And so, in this little parable of the tortoise, struck by a car, opposed by all the natural elements, the tortoise can be said to represent the People. It struggles on indomitably as though driven by a superior power. Whether it reaches its destination or not does not really seem to matter. Its meaning is in the struggle.

CHAPTER 4

Summary

Tom Joad takes a sip of whiskey from the pint he is carrying in his pocket, removes his shoes and plods along the dusty road in his bare feet. He notices the high-domed shell of a land turtle crawling slowly along, picks it up, examines it, and rolls it up in his coat as a present for the kids.

Tom heads for the shelter of a willow tree and finds that the spot is already occupied by Jim Casy, the preacher who baptized him. Jim is stretched out in the shade singing "Yes, sir, that's my savior" to the tune of "Yes, Sir, That's My Baby." Casy has a neck as stringy as a celery stalk, an abnormally high forehead and eloquent hands.

Casy recognizes Tom as "ol' Tom's Boy." When Tom realizes that Casy is the preacher, Casy corrects him. He used to be a preacher, he says, "a Burning Busher" who used to "howl out the name of Jesus to glory", but those days are over Casy says: "Just Jim Casy now. Ain't got the call no more. Got a lot of sinful idears — but they seem kinda sensible."

Tom offers Casy a "snort" of his "fact'ry liquor" and Casy explains that the "spirit" is still strong in him, but it isn't the same as before, because now he "ain't so sure of a lot of things." Noticing the turtle struggling under Tom's coat, Casy observes that no one can keep a turtle, because they keep working and working until they finally escape. Like the turtle, Casy feels he has questioned the old gospel "until I got it all tore down." Though he gets the "spirit" sometimes, he has nothing to preach about, and though he has the call to lead the people, he has no place to lead them.

Casy feels like a hypocrite, because after he had worked the people up to such a frenzy of jumping, talking in tongues and glory shouting that they would fall down and lose consciousness, he would revive some and then take one of the girls out in the grass and lay with her. Besides making him feel like a damned hypocrite, these incidents presented Casy with a dilemma: laying with a girl was supposed to be the devil's work, but "the more grace a girl got in her, the quicker she wants to go out in the grass." Tom observes that maybe he should have been a preacher himself.

But Casy continues to think aloud. He has come to the conclusion, he says, that there is no such thing as sin and virtue. Whatever people do, whether it be "nice" or not is all part of the same thing. Moreover, Casy continues, hoping Tom will not be offended, what need is there to be always referring things to God or Jesus. Perhaps the "Holy Sperit" is really the human spirit, man's love for his fellow man. Perhaps, he concludes, all men have one big soul and everybody is a part of it.

Tom observes that Casy could never have church meetings with ideas like that, because people would refuse to accept them. They want real revivals with plenty of jumping and yelling.

When Casy asks Tom how his father is, Tom admits that he does not know because he has been in prison for four years and he has received no mail from him. Tom tells Casy how he killed a man in a drunken brawl after the man had knifed him. He is on parole now after serving four years of a seven-year sentence. Tom tells Casy that prison wasn't too bad in some ways. There were regular meals, clean clothes, and places to take a bath.

Tom and the preacher amble along in the late afternoon light. Casy remarks that there would have been a good corn crop this year if the dust had not come, and Tom observes that every year he can remember there was a good crop coming, but it never came.

Tom explains how his father, grandfather and brother Noah stole their house when it was abandoned by another family. Unable to tow the whole house away, they cut it in half only to find upon their return that a neighbor had stolen the other half.

The Joad place finally comes into view but, even from a distance, Tom and Casy realize that something is wrong. No one is there.

Commentary

This chapter introduces the ex-preacher Jim Casy, another of the three main characters in the novel. Jim Casy's initials are probably meant to suggest his Christ-like qualities which become more pronounced toward the end of the story. Like Emerson, Casy discovers the Oversoul through intuition and rejects his congregation so as to better embrace all men. Sensing an apparent contradiction in someone being able to sin while under the influence of the "sperit," Casy concludes that it is not too important whether one has the spirit of God or of Jesus. What is important is the human spirit, an awareness of and love for one's neighbor. In the final analysis it is not abstract concepts that matter so much as the actions of human beings. It is this realization of the importance of human values which later prompts Casy to join the migrants. He wants to help.

CHAPTER 5

Summary

In this intercalary chapter Steinbeck outlines the legal and economic factors which forced owner and tenant alike to abandon obsolete farming techniques and outmoded ways of life. In the great upheaval caused by the Oklahoma Dust Bowl, the landowners are pitted against the tenant farmers, and both are forced to do the bidding of the man-made monster, the bank, which no man can seem to control. All of them "were caught in something larger than themselves."

The desperate farmers plead for a little more time, hopeful that the next year will be a good one. With all the wars and the need for explosives and uniforms, they argue, the price of cotton may skyrocket. But the banks cannot live on hope. "The bank — the monster has to have profits all the time. It can't wait. It'll die. No, taxes go on. When the monster stops growing, it dies. It can't stay one size."

Finally the owners explain that the tenant system will work no longer. All the small farms have to be grouped together and one man on a tractor will take the place of twelve or fourteen families. The owners will pay the tractor driver a wage and take all the crop. True, in a few years the land will be killed with cotton crops. But then it can be sold to families in the East.

When the tenants realize that they are going to be "tractored out," they protest that their forefathers fought the Indians for this land, cleared it and cultivated it. They and their children have been born on this land and have worked and died on it. They own it. "That's what makes it ours — being born on it, working it, dying on it. That makes ownership, not a paper with numbers on it."

Many of the owners are commiserating with the tenants' plight. They hate what they have to do. But there is no way out of the dilemma. The tenants must go. Perhaps, they suggest, the farmers might find work picking cotton "over the line." Or, better still, why don't they go west to California? There's plenty of work there, they say, and the living is easy.

The huge diesel tractors arrive and begin plowing straight through the land, "through fences, through door-yards, in and out of gullies in straight lines." The man driving the tractor, gloved and goggled, looks like a robot, part of the monster. Not having worked the land with a team of horses, he feels no love for the land. When the driver stops for lunch the tenant gets a closer look at him and recognizes him as a neighbor's boy. How can he do such work against his own people? The driver replies that he needs the money. He is paid three dollars a day and he has a wife and children to provide for. He knows that for every day's work he does, fifteen or twenty families have to leave their homes and wander the roads, but he can't think of such things, times are changing. There is no room for the little farmer any more.

When the driver tells the tenant that his house is in the way and that he will have to knock it down, the tenant threatens to shoot him if he dares to come too close. The driver observes laconically that if the tenant does shoot him, the tenant will hang, and before he is hanged someone else will be driving the tractor and he will bump the house down instead. The farmer, utterly exasperated by his inability to fight the forces which are destroying him, adopts a more conciliatory attitude. "We all got to figure. There's some way to stop this. It's not like lightning or earthquakes. We've got a bad thing made by men, and by God that's something we can change."

The tractor thunders on, gouging long straight furrows. It eventually crushes the house, and grinds on while the tenant, rifle in hand, and his family, stare after it.

Commentary

This is a strongly naturalistic chapter with its emphasis on a form of socio-economic determinism which has gripped both the tenants and the owners. Steinbeck portrays man as the victim of environmental forces and the product of social and economic factors beyond his control or full understanding. The beleaguered tenants are powerless before the economic monster which is choking them. They cannot get angry at the owners because they merely represent the banks and the banks in turn take orders from some vague interests "in the East."

All, to some extent, are subservient to the monster which takes different forms, the Oklahoma land company, a bank, a tractor. The monster absorbs its members, drains them of their individualities, and makes them into organization men.

The Joads are swept up in this great upheaval much like the turtle in Chapter 3 which is buffeted and stymied in its relentless march towards some instinctive goal in the southwest.

CHAPTER 6

Summary

Tom and Jim Casy stand on the hill looking down on the Joad house. They can see that the house has been smashed in at one corner and knocked off its foundations, so that the entire structure leans at an angle. All the fences have been taken down and the outhouse lies on its side. The barn is empty, except for the mice and a few discarded farm articles. The place is deserted. Tom and Jim go into the abandoned house to look for a note or a clue that will tell them the whereabouts of the Joad family.

Tom sees a lean cat wandering around, and he realizes that there aren't any neighbors left either: if there were, the cat would have moved in with them. Moreover, no one has taken any lumber or window frames from the obviously deserted homestead. There must be no one left for miles.

Tom remembers that he still has the turtle and, having no more use for it, releases it. The turtle immediately heads out on its original course, southwest.

As the sun begins to set, Casy notices someone coming through the cotton, moving in a cloud of dust. Finally Tom recognizes the newcomer as Muley Graves, an old friend. Muley tells Tom where his parents have gone. After putting up a last fight for their land, during which Tom's grandfather blasted the lights off the invading tractor with a rifle, the Joad family moved to Tom's Uncle John's place. Everyone, including Grampa, has been chopping cotton and saving money to buy a car and go west.

Casy asks Muley why people are being kicked off the land. Muley explains bitterly that the "dirty sons-a-bitches," the landowners, decided that they could no longer afford to keep tenants, because the share a tenant gets is just the margin of profit the owners need to survive. The owners concluded that if they made one huge farm of all the small holdings they could just barely make it pay. Then they proceeded to tractor-out all the families.

Though Muley has been entirely dispossessed, he adamantly refuses to leave the land. Tom is surprised that his father left so easily and that his Grampa did not kill someone. Muley explains that no one knew how to fight. Finding themselves up against a vague entity called a "company," in Muley's words, "Got a fella crazy. There wan't nobody you could lay for."

24

Since Uncle John's place is eight miles away and Tom is tired of walking, he suggests to Muley that they go to his place, about a mile away, for the night. Muley replies that his wife and children and her brother have all left for California and there is nothing to eat at his place. Tom, who has become accustomed to regular prison meals, is famished, and he shrewdly asks Muley how he has been finding food. Muley admits that for a while he ate frogs, squirrels and sometimes prairie dogs, but now he has organized a little trapline and he catches rabbits and prairic chickens as well as skunks and raccoons. Muley produces two cotton tails and a jackrabbit from the sack he has been carrying, and decides to share them with Casy and Tom, because "if a fella's got somepin to eat an' another fella's hungry — why the first fella ain't got no choice." Casy observes that "Muley's got a-holt of somepin, an, it's too big for him, an' it's too big for me."

Tom cleans the rabbits expertly and roasts them over an open fire. While the meal is cooking, Muley explains how he has been moving around the country "like a damn ol' graveyard ghos," haunting the scenes of his boyhood, the spot where he first made love, the spot down by the barn where his father was gored to death by a bull, and the room where his son was born. Muley hates the landowners for destroying these things by forcing people to live on roads in piled-up cars.

Casy is moved by Muley's impassioned attack on the landowners to restate his growing conviction that he should join the migrants and help them in a practical way. They eat ravenously and Tom tells Casy and Muley about prison life. He says that if he had to kill again in self-protection, he would do so, and adds that a prison term has taught him nothing.

Muley notices headlights bobbing up into the dark sky and tells the others they must hide because they are trespassing. Tom does so reluctantly, crawling into the cotton on a patch of land his family once cultivated. Since he is on parole, he cannot afford a fight with the law. The deputies arrive, put out the fire and scan the surroundings with a spotlight, but Muley, who is used to their tricks, outwits them.

Later, Muley leads them to a safe place to spend the night, a cave which Tom remembers digging with his brother Noah.

Commentary

This chapter presents us with a concrete example of the general events referred to in Chapter 5. The Joads have been swept up in the great socio-economic squeeze, their house is destroyed, and they are forced to move. Muley Graves lingers on, a personification of the graves of ancestors being left behind. He is stubborn, as his nickname indicates, and he refuses to leave the country although he has no house to live in. Muley has become more of a hunted animal than a human being, and he is able to subsist only by adopting animal habits.

Here, also, Tom frees the turtle which immediately continues on its way toward the southwest, the same direction in which the Joads will go.

When Muley shares his hard-won meal with Tom and Casy, he observes that a man who has something just has to share with one who has nothing. It is this sense of *noblesse oblige* which will keep the Joads and thousands of families like them existing on the very edge of subsistence. Like the turtle, they do not understand their actions, their instinctive drive towards a common goal, but Casy verbalizes their actions into the belief that all people are just part of one great being. It is not until Tom is forced to retreat from the advancing deputies, that he realizes the true meaning of his parole. He can no longer act as a free man and, as such, he is prevented from following his natural instincts. This restraining force will modify his actions later on, in California.

CHAPTER 7

Summary

In this intercalary chapter, Steinbeck presents another aspect of the great migration, the necessity for some means of transportation. Crooked used-car dealers are taking advantage of the people's distress and selling them anything that rolls off the lot. The author presents the point of view of the greedy, used-car dealer trying to make as much profit as possible while the boom lasts.

Used cars are lined up on lots and salesmen are selling them as rapidly as possible. There is no time to be wasted on people who are just looking — they take your time and don't leave a dime. There seems to be a larger profit and turnover in used cars than in new ones. The dealer always tries to take out the good battery before he makes delivery and, if the gears or transmissions are making a lot of noise, he pours sawdust inside to cut down the racket. The dealer prefers to deal with the tenant farmer who knows nothing about cars and who will sign promissory notes at high interest rates. If something goes wrong with the car, it is easy to ignore a sharecropper's complaints. Besides, the customer is leaving the state. The salesman's cynical predatory attitude is summed up in his two mottoes: "If I had enough jalopies I'd retire in six months" and "We sell 'em, but we don't push 'em home."

Commentary

This disturbing little chapter again shows how the profit motive can set man against man and forecasts the difficulty the Joads must face when they buy a car to take them west.

CHAPTER 8

Summary

Casy and Tom are walking to Uncle John's place in a feeble pre-dawn light, having been awakened by Muley, who warned them to be off the land by sunrise. Tom thinks Muley might be "nuts," acting as he does as though "Injuns were after him," but Casy is not so sure. Something menacing seems to be in the air.

They begin discussing Tom's Uncle John whom Tom describes as the "lonest goddam man in the world." John has been "sort of wild" ever since he lost his young bride of four months. He blames himself for her death because he failed to get a doctor when she had an acute appendicitis which he mistook for a common case of indigestion. Ever since, he has been trying to overcome his feelings of guilt by giving away nearly everything he owns. Seeing his old dog, Flash, mating with a bitch in the road reminds Tom of an earthy joke which he proceeds to tell Casy. Casy enjoys the joke, relieved that he is no longer a preacher and can feel free to laugh at such things. He tells Tom that he "cusses" any time he feels like it now, and has discovered that "it does a fella good to cuss if he wants to."

Tom and Casy find the Joads busy preparing to leave for California. Old Tom Joad is working on a Hudson Super-six sedan which has been ripped in two with a cold chisel and been converted into a makeshift truck. The truck is loaded with farm equipment to be sold in town. Old Tom is overjoyed to see his son and relieved to hear that he has not broken out of jail, but has been duly paroled and granted his "papers." They decide to suprise Mrs. Joad who is preparing breakfast in the kitchen, and old Tom tells her that a couple of fellows have just come along the road looking for a bite to eat. Without any hesitation Ma welcomes the two "strangers" stipulating only that they have to wash their hands.

Ma is heavy and thick with child-bearing, but not fat. She has thin, steel-gray hair gathered in a wispy knot at the back of her head. Her full face is not soft, but controlled and kindly. Ma is obviously the backbone of the family, shielding them all from fear by denying it in herself, finding joy and laughter in the smallest things so that they, watching her, can also be joyful. "She seemed to know that if she swayed, the family shook, and if she ever deeply wavered or despaired the family would fall, the family will to function would be gone." Ma is almost stunned with the surprise of seeing Tom. She had dreaded the idea of leaving him behind and had worried that, once they had left, Tom might never find them again.

Tom asks where Granma and Grampa are and learns that they sleep in the barn to avoid disturbing the children when they have to get up in the night. Ma is relieved when Tom assures her that prison has not made him bitter or "crazy mad." She was afraid he might have been hurt like Pretty Boy Floyd who was tormented so much by his jailers that he turned into a mad coyote and had to be run down and killed. Tom expresses anger at the way their house had been destroyed, but Ma cautions him against fighting the authorities alone. He would just be hunted down like a coyote. Ma cannot help wondering just the same what might happen if the hundred thousand people who have now been dispossessed were "all mad the same way." If that were the case, no one would be hunted down. Tom has never heard his mother talk this way before, but she reminds him that she has never had her house pushed over before, never had her family abandoned on the road, and never had to sell everything.

Grampa arrives, a lean, ragged, quick old man who is always having trouble buttoning his fly. He is a cantankerous, complaining, mischievous, lecherous old fellow who can be vicious and cruel but is somehow very amusing even when he gives in to his baser instincts, which is most of the time.

Behind Grampa hobbles Granma, "who had survived only because she was as mean as her husband." In a moment of religious fervor Granma had fired both barrels of a shotgun at her husband, relieving him of a substantial portion of one buttock. Since then Grampa has admired his wife and stopped trying to torture her as children torture bugs.

Granma and Grampa are followed by Pa and Noah. Noah, the first born, is tall and strange, always bearing a look of wonder in his face. Noah has never been angry in his life. He speaks slowly and seldom, but is not stupid, just strange. He has little pride and no sexual urges. Pa thinks he is responsible for Noah's strangeness because, when Noah was being born, Pa had pulled and twisted the infant in an effort to ease his wife's terrible pain. The midwife, arriving late, had righted matters by remolding the misshapen child, but Pa always remembered and was ashamed.

Grampa greets Tom with a volley of obscenity, obviously proud of his "jailbird" grandson. Granma can only "pu-raise Gawd fur vittory." The preliminaries over, Grampa crowds past everyone, loads his plate with pork, biscuits and gravy and stuffs his mouth full before anyone else can get in.

Tom remembers Casy, who has moved off a distance to give the family a little privacy. When Granma learns the preacher is around, she demands a "grace." Casy protests that he is no longer a preacher, but he is willing to give a very general thanks for being glad to be there and being with people who are kind and generous. Casy says that he is as confused as Jesus was in the wilderness. But somehow he has identified himself with all things. And he knows now that men are holy when they all work and cooperate together.

They all crunch and slurp their way through breakfast and the men go out to inspect the truck. Pa assures Tom that his brother Al, who has a knack for mechanical things, checked the machine before they bought it and found it to be satisfactory. Al is out, Pa said. He is sixteen now and thinks of nothing but girls and engines. Grampa joins the conversation to brag that he was worse when he was Al's age. He feels he will be rejuvenated when he gets to California and starts eating oranges and grapes.

Tom learns that Ruthie and Winfield, the youngest Joad children, are in town (Sallisaw, Oklahoma) selling equipment with their Uncle John. Another sister, Rose of Sharon (called Rosasharn), is staying with the Rivers family since she is now married to Connie Rivers and is expecting a baby. The men make plans to start their trek west soon.

Al struts up cockily until he recognizes his heroic brother Tom, whom he admires immensely for having killed a man. Al drops the swagger and begins to imitate Tom's prison-face stoicism. He is disappointed when he learns that Tom has not broken out of prison but has been paroled.

Commentary

This long chapter is important for plot and characterization. It is rather significant that Steinbeck introduces all the remaining members of the family in one unit since it is this unity which Ma will strive so hard to maintain. Tom's reunion with his parents, especially with Ma, is intensely moving. Ma Joad is, with her son Tom and Casy, one of the three main characters of the novel. Ma feels Tom's face as a blind person might, a foreshadowing of her later farewell to Tom in the dark California culvert cave (Chapter 18). She is deeply grateful for Tom's unexpected arrival because she feared they would have to leave without him and the family would be incomplete from the outset.

Both Ma and Casy make tentative, faltering advances in their awareness of the universal brotherhood of man. Ma expresses an idea which will become a dominant motif later in California. What if all the sharecroppers were to unite? Could the authorities then persecute any one in particular? And Casy, while saying grace, arrives at the conclusion that men are truly holy when they are all working together.

Grampa, Granma, Pa, Noah, and Al are all skilfully introduced and sketched in Chapter 8. Through a clever use of detail and dialect, Steinbeck clothes each character with his own unique individuality. Because these characters are so believable we are less inclined to question the underlying didactic elements which make this a proletarian novel and a naturalistic document. Steinbeck's characters seem to stumble over vaguely formulated principles which are all the more forceful because only partially perceived by the very people in whose lives the principles are finding expression.

The Biblical structure of the migration (Egypt, Exodus, Canaan) is supported by a continuous series of symbols and symbolic actions. The most recurrent symbolism is that of grapes. Grampa wants to go to California and squash grapes all over his face. This novel's title, taken from 'The Battle Hymn of the Republic', is itself a reference to Revelation (14:19) "And the angel thrust in his sharp sickle into the earth, and gathered the vineyard of the earth, and cast it into the great press of the wrath of God."

CHAPTER 9

Summary

The tenants are shown picking over their possessions for the journey west. The men are ruthless because the past has been spoiled, but the women know they will recall the past and they try to cling to their memories by preserving little mementos. Good farm equipment and animals are being sold for a fraction of their value. And with each sale goes a bitter curse, a curse on all the powers which take advantage of another man's desperation.

Everything but the barest essentials must be left behind. The rest is piled high in the yards and burned. And then everyone must leave quickly, because the past has been destroyed, and nothing remains but the fearful rush towards an uncertain future.

Commentary

This short chapter, like other intercalary ones, is a commentary in itself. Steinbeck manages to soften the didactic element through a combination of stream of consciousness technique interspersed with graphic description. In Chapter VII, he adopted the point of view of the used-car salesman. Here, he invites the reader to look at the scenes of desolation through the eyes of the tenant farmers and their families who must leave behind all but the barest essentials. This approach permits him to describe the scenes vividly while making general observations from the architectonic viewpoint of the author. Thus, after following the reasonings of the woman who must leave behind her *Pilgrim's Progress*, her father's pipe, a picture of an angel, the china dog that Aunt Sadie brought from the St. Louis Fair, a letter from a dead brother and an old-time hat, Steinbeck makes the observation which sums up the agony of such situations: "How can we live without our lives? How will we know it's us without our past? No, leave it. Burn it."

Like the previous odd-numbered chapters, this intercalary chapter pre-figures the specific plight of the Joads. They too must make the agonizing decisions required of such a migration, selling their farm equipment for a pittance and parting with their most cherished possessions.

CHAPTER 10

Summary

The truck has left with everything to be sold. Tom moons about the homestead until Ma, who is doing the family washing, asks if he thinks things will be all right in California. She has seen the handbills advertising for workers and heard the stories about high wages to be earned picking fruit, but she is still worried about what they will really find at the end of their 2000-mile journey. "I'm scared of stuff so nice," she tells Tom. "I ain't got faith. I'm scared something ain't so nice about it."

Grampa gets up, crochety as ever. He is keen to get to California and work again picking fruit. Perhaps he will find his brother, who stole a Colt revolver from him when he left for California forty years before.

Casy approaches Tom and Ma and asks with some embarrassment if he could go west with the Joad family. Ma says she would be proud to have him, but the matter is for the men to decide at the family council meeting. Casy tells her he has given up preaching and wants to live among real people, and learn from them. He wants to " 'hear the poetry of folks talkin'.' "

Late in the afternoon the truck comes back, covered with dust. Ruthie and Winfield bounce out of the truck bed, excited about meeting their older brother again. Beside them is Rose of Sharon, careful and dignified, changed by pregnancy from the provocative and passionate girl Connie Rivers had married. Al has been driving, with Pa and Uncle John — the heads of the clan — sitting beside him. The older men are angry and sad; they have gotten only eighteen dollars for every moveable thing from the farm. They were not experienced at "merchandising" and the buyer had outsmarted them. They know the family will be disappointed.

In the evening light, the family council begins, with all the Joads gathered at the truck. The ancient Hudson, which is to take them to California, is now their only home. Pa tells them they have a total of $154 dollars. Al reports on the state of the Hudson. The battery has been replaced and the gearbox is free of sawdust. The tires are no good, but they are a popular size and easy to obtain. The older men agree that Al has done well, and Al smiles with relief. They argue as to whether or not to take the preacher along. Pa says they do not have room; altogether they are already taking twelve people. Ma responds firmly that they can always feed an extra mouth, since they have two pigs and over a hundred dollars. When they call Casy over, he knows he has been taken into the family.

It is deep dusk when the men begin the slaughtering of the pigs, a job that must be completed before they can leave. When done, they decide to begin packing immediately so they can start at dawn. Noah and Ma start cutting and salting the slabs of meat; Rose of Sharon brings out all the family's clothing; Tom gathers all their remaining tools. The preacher takes over from Ma, even though she tells him that salting pigs is "woman's work," and she goes to get the kitchen utensils, knives and forks ready. Little things, such as which pan to take, become important as they try to organize themselves for this new situation.

Later Ma walks heavily into the stripped bedroom. She takes out an old and soiled stationery box. Here are her memories — letters, photographs, clippings and trinkets. She sorts out the ring, earrings, a watch charm and one gold cuff-link, puts them in an envelope to keep, tenderly closes the box and burns it in the stove.

Pa and Al load the truck carefully. Al decides that as soon as he can he will fix the big tarpaulin with a ridge-pole so that those in the truck bed will be out of the sun. By dawn they are ready.

The dogs start to bark when Muley Graves comes into the yard. He refuses Pa's offer to go with the Joads, and only asks them to look up his folks. At this point Grampa announces that he is not going to California either. Oklahoma is his country: "I b'long here. An I don't give a goddamn if they's oranges an' grapes crowdin' a fella outa bed even. . . . This country ain't no good, but it's my country." Tom and Ma and Pa have no whiskey to get the old man drunk, so they put a children's "soothin' syrup" into his coffee to put him to sleep until they can be on their way.

The time has come to go. The family are now afraid, reluctant to take the first active step. Then the numbness breaks. Ma and Granma get into the front seat beside Al. The others climb aboard the loaded truck bed until the springs lie flat under the weight. They take one dog and leave the chickens and the two other dogs with Muley. Al starts the truck and it shudders across the yard. Ma thinks of looking back, but the load blocks her view, so she sets her eyes straight onto the road ahead. The rest of them watch the last wisps of smoke rising from the chimney and wave to Muley as the truck crawls slowly westward through the dust.

Commentary

This is an important chapter in the book because it depicts a crucial event in the life of the Joad family: the setting out for California. They are caught between a past which can no longer support them and an unknown future. They move between enthusiasm and inertia, letting hope accompanied by suffering triumph over practical anticipation. Steinbeck gives these swings of emotion an almost physical illustration in his description of the collective action on the night they decide to leave: they plan to slaughter the pigs and wait till morning to pack; then decide to pack immediately and leave at first light. The family is swept along to a decision that is inevitable, but which they really do not want to make.

It is also a key chapter in the way it deals with some of the individual characters. Grampa's wish to recover his lost Colt revolver and his lost youth in California is symbolic. Neither are going to happen. In fact, Grampa is correct when he states that Oklahoma is his country; he won't survive long after he is removed from his roots. His unconscious condition when they drive away is part of the death that will soon follow. Grampa symbolizes the past that the family is leaving behind.

Two characters are outside the family and they make different symbolic decisions. Muley Graves remains with the past in Oklahoma, but Jim Casy asks to join the family. His hard-found interest in seeking the poetry in people's speech foreshadows the way in which his character will expand and develop throughout the novel.

CHAPTER 11

Summary

When the people and their farm animals leave the land and are replaced by tractors and artificial fertilizers, the "wonder" goes out of work and the land is no longer something personal. In the abandoned houses, bats, mice, owls, cats and weeds take over. The wind pries off shingles, and gradually the homes fall apart.

Commentary

This short chapter emphasizes the desolation which results when the delicate balance of human beings, their land, and their homes is upset. As Grampa is dying as a result of leaving the land, so the land, which once seemed almost human, becomes vacant and sterile.

CHAPTER 12

Summary

The main artery connecting Sallisaw, Oklahoma, to Bakersfield, California, is called Highway 66. This is the "road of flight" for a quarter of a million migrants in fifty thousand jalopies. The drivers listen carefully to the motor, the wheels, the tappets, terrified that something may break far from a town. It's California or bust, and every road-weary Okie keeps his courage up with a vision of the orange groves and vineyards awaiting him. Every now and then a part breaks or a tire blows, and the travellers are forced to pay outrageous prices for replacements. Like all great hardships, the migration brings out the worst and the best in men.

Commentary

Steinbeck gives us, for the first time, an intercalary chapter without a narrative chapter preceding it. Chapter 11 was a symbolic farewell to Oklahoma. Chapter 12, which does not mention the Joads, is the beginning of a new structural unit, roughly the second third of the novel. The Joads will soon join this river of suffering humanity moving west to the Promised Land of California.

CHAPTER 13

Summary

Al is driving the overloaded Hudson with Ma and Granma beside him in the front seat. He listens carefully for the least sound or shudder which might indicate an imminent breakdown. Al is afraid they may run into hills and he will be unable to make the grade because of their heavy load. Ma tells him she seems to recall hearing that there are hills ahead, even mountains. Al suggests that perhaps they should not have brought the preacher, but Ma assures him that he will be glad that Casy came along because the preacher will help them. Al asks his mother whether she is apprehensive about what may lie ahead, but she insists that she is merely concentrating on the road going by and wondering when the family will be looking for more pork bones to chew on.

Granma wakes up and insists she has to get out of the car. Al stops near some bushes and the others, sunburned and weary, let themselves down from the truck. Grampa regains consciousness momentarily but he thinks he is still back home on the farm. Ma decides to pass around a pan of pork bones, but they soon discover there is no water and a mild panic seizes everyone as they suddenly become conscious of their thirst. Al assures them they will get water at the first service station they come to. They clamber aboard and the truck moves on.

They stop at a roadside shack with two gas pumps in front of it. The stout, red-faced owner is about to refuse them water when Al assures him they need gas and that they are not begging. The owner is disappointed that he is not able to attract any of the big new cars to his station. Most people who stop at his place have no money and want to trade personal possessions for gasoline. Casy points out that it is not the people's fault, and the owner agrees, but he still wonders what the country is coming to. Casy tries to answer the somewhat rhetorical question. He tells the owner that he has been walking around the country and he has decided that people don't "come" to anything, but that they are always on the way to something. People are moving, he reasons aloud, because they want something better than they have, and the only way to find it is to go out and get it. The owner accepts Casy's explanation, but he is not satisfied with the answer. He still wants to know what things are coming to. This attitude angers Al, who accuses the owner of not listening. Al looks at the rusty gas pump and the shack behind it painted yellow to imitate the big company stations in town, and he realizes that the fat man is a failure.

The fat man admits that he is already thinking of going west, and Casy assures him that everyone is in the same boat. Casy confides that he used to expend all his energy fighting the devil "'cause I figgered the devil was the enemy." But something worse than the devil has a grip on the country and, like a terrible Gila monster, "it ain't gonna let go until it's chopped loose."

Connie and Rose of Sharon go through a little ritual of getting a drink of water. They are both living in a world of their own, enthralled by the promise of new life. Though Rose is not very thirsty, she decides that perhaps she should drink for the baby's sake. Connie is very solicitous as they talk of buying a new car one day, but first a house.

The dog wanders onto the highway and is run over by a big swift car. Rose associates the animal's suffering with her coming ordeal and asks Connie whether it will hurt. Connie assures her that it will not. The gas station owner promises to bury the dog and, after rounding up Granma who has fallen asleep in the outhouse, the family piles on top of the truck again. Al reluctantly allows Tom to take over the steering wheel after cautioning him on all the danger signs to watch for.

As they drive through Oklahoma City, Ruthie and Winfield are frightened by the bigness and the strangeness of it all. Ma is worried about Tom crossing the state line and thus breaking his parole. Tom assures her he will be all right as long as he doesn't commit any crimes. Tom sees some people with an old touring car camping alongside the road and decides to pull up beside them as it is just about sundown and time to eat and bed down for the night. A lean, middle-aged man is looking at the motor of the touring car. When Tom asks him whether the Joads can stop there for the night, the man explains that the only reason they have stopped is " 'cause this goddam ol' trap wouldn' go no further." Still, Tom insists, the others were there first, and they have a right to decide whether or not they want neighbors. When he puts the matter in this light, the man smiles and extends a warm greeting. He calls to his wife, "Sairy," who emerges from their tent. Sairy is a small, wizened woman, obviously not well.

Tom drives the truck off the road and Ma immediately begins to organize things for supper, sending Ruthie and Winfield off to a nearby gas station for a bucket of water. The new neighbors introduce themselves as the Wilsons from Kansas. Grampa is sick and Sairy Wilson offers him the hospitality of their tent. Grampa begins to cry as they help him into the shelter, and Ma asks Casy to take a look at the old man. Casy and Sairy kneel beside Grampa and decide that he is about to have a stroke. Granma insists on going into the tent where she maintains Grampa is not sick but merely sulking. When Casy assures her that Grampa is really sick, Granma asks him why he isn't praying then, since he's a preacher. Casy objects that he isn't a preacher any longer, that he doesn't know what to pray for or who to pray to. As Grampa goes into convulsions, Granma hops about yelling at Casy "Pray, goddam you!"

Casy begins the Lord's Prayer and, before he is finished, the old man is dead. All is still as Granma leaves the tent, her head held high. Gradually the family council gathers. They thank the Wilsons for the last bit of comfort they were able to give Grampa, and Al volunteers that he and Tom will repair the Wilson car to show the family's appreciation. The problem now is what to do with the body. The Joads have only a hundred and fifty dollars left and if they report the death as the law demands, they will either have to pay an undertaker forty dollars or have Grampa buried as a pauper. If they spend the money on the undertaker they will not have enough to reach California. They decide that, in this case, the law cannot be followed, and Pa feels he has the right to bury his own father. Casy sums up the situation when he says "Law changes, but 'got-to's' go on. You got the right to do what you got to do." Tom suggests they bury a note with Grampa telling who he is, how he died, and why he is buried there. He is afraid someone may find the body, think Grampa has been killed, and cause trouble because "The gov'ment's got more interest in a dead man than a live one."

Ma lays out the body while Sairy gets supper. They wrap Grampa in a quilt and lay him in a deep grave the men have dug. Tom adds a suitable text from Scripture to the vital statistics and the note is placed in a fruit jar next to the body. They again prevail upon Casy to say a few words, and he reasons aloud that it doesn't really matter whether Grampa was good or bad in life. The main point is that he did live. Casy sees no point in praying for an old man who is dead. If he were to pray, he says, it would be for the people who are still alive and don't know which way to turn.

The family eats in silence, staring into the fire. Rose of Sharon goes off to comfort Granma who begins to whimper. Al thinks it's a shame that Grampa will never have the grapes he longed for, but Casy points out that Grampa died the minute he left home.

Mr. Wilson says that they have been on the road for three weeks and have had all kinds of car trouble. When Sairy took ill they had to stop for ten days. Wilson still feels the trek is worth the effort because he has seen handbills advertising work for fruit pickers, and he is looking forward to a job where he can eat all he wants. Pa takes out a handbill of his own asking for 800 workers to pick peas. When Wilson recognizes the handbill as the same one he saw, Pa points out that California is a big state and, even if they get all the workers they need to pick peas, there will be plenty of other jobs.

Tom and Al suggest sharing loads with the Wilsons and keeping together on the road. That way they can all get west. Everyone likes the idea except Sairy who has been ill and fears a relapse. Ma reassures her and they all go to sleep — all but Sairy, who stares into the sky and nurses her pain.

Commentary

The Odyssey has begun, and a strange new world is opening up for the Joads. As though to symbolize this disorientation, the dog, unaccustomed to the highway, strays away and is killed — next, Grampa has a stroke and dies. Like the dog which was familiar only with the open spaces, Grampa cannot stand the shock of leaving his homeland. Finally, Rose of Sharon has a premonition of the tragedy awaiting her. She fears for her baby which is later born dead.

While the death of Grampa signals the breaking up of the smaller family unit, the cooperation between the Wilsons and the Joads suggests that the individual family is being replaced by a larger concept of a world family. This is what Casy has been tending towards, and his agonizing reappraisal is gradually finding concrete expression in the trip west. His Emersonian prayer for the living rather than for the dead is a direct consequence of his belief that all that lives is holy.

Ma was right when she told Al he would be glad they had brought the preacher along. Casy "says" grace for the family, assists Grampa on his deathbed and helps bury the old man. Later, in California, Casy surrenders himself to the sheriff so that Tom will not be suspected. Casy's main role, however, transcends the rendering of such services. In his own groping way, he expresses the great sorrow and deep longings the Okies have for a decent life and their rightful share of happiness and prosperity. Without Casy, the great migration to the southwest would make as little sense as the relentless push of the land turtle.

CHAPTER 14

Summary

The radical change that is sweeping America makes the great western landowners nervous and fearful. They are struggling against government interference, increased labor unity and higher taxes — the causes of which are simple and relate to the hunger and frustration, multiplied a million times, of men and women who want their share in a better life.

Families have borrowed money from the bank, and now the bank wants the land. The banks send tractors to work the land, and to drive the farmers away. In the beginning, it was "one man, one family, driven from the land." Now there are thousands of families turned away from the land all across the country. The claim, "I lost my land" is changing to a chorus of "We lost our land." The great Western States are afraid of this change from "I" to "We."

CHAPTER 15

Summary

Steinbeck describes the typical hamburger stand, the closest thing to an oasis in a desert of winding road. They are all the same — two gasoline pumps out front, a screen door, a long bar, stools and a foot rail. Customers may play the slot machine, put a nickel in the phonograph, buy razor blades, pie, coffee or alka seltzer.

Mae and Al run this particular establishment. Mae is the contact who smiles at truck drivers because they are the backbone of the business. Al, more taciturn, tends to his griddle. Cars from every state whiz by on Highway 66. Some contain rich, pampered, discontented women and little pot-bellied men in light suits and panama hats. They are tourists going to look at the mountains, see the Pacific, lie on the beaches and be disappointed and bored because they have lost their zest for living and their capacity to wonder. Mae calls these people "shitheels" because they stop for a drink, complain that it isn't cold enough, then use a half dozen paper napkins.

Two truck drivers come in, play a Crosby hit on the phonograph, joke with Mae, try the slot machine and order pie and coffee. They tell a few jokes and relate the terrible details of an accident they have seen that morning. A lone man driving a Cadillac rammed his speeding car into a truck loaded with migrants and their belongings. Mae wonders why all the people are going out west.

A 1926 Nash sedan, part of the migrant caravan, pulls wearily off the highway. The occupants, a man, his wife and two boys, need water and want to buy a loaf of bread, but they cannot spare enough money for a whole loaf. Upon Al's insistence, Mae finally gives in and sells them a fifteen-cent loaf of bread for a dime. The man, obviously embarrassed by the necessity of being so thrifty, explains that they have a thousand miles to go and he is not at all sure whether they will make it. When Mae sells the boys some candy for a fraction of its cost, the two truck drivers more than compensate the institution by leaving two half-dollars as tips. Al, who keeps a record of when a slot machine is ready to pay, plays a few nickles into the one the truckers have been feeding the most and hits the jackpot.

As Mae wonders what all the people will do in California, another truck pulls up and the whole pie and coffee routine starts up again.

Commentary

This is the longest intercalary chapter and it presents several strikingly diverse views of humanity in a series of vivid, staccato scenes. Steinbeck first develops a devastating sketch of the blasé, complaining rich in their huge automobiles. All they can think of as they speed past the seemingly endless caravan of destitutes is how they will enjoy themselves in the pleasure spots of California. The abrupt switch to the poor family in the overloaded Nash provides a brutal contrast which is softened by the generosity of the truck drivers.

CHAPTER 16

Summary

The Joads and Wilsons settle into a pattern of living. With the truck in the lead, they drive through the Texas Panhandle and into New Mexico. Then the Wilson car burns out a connecting-rod bearing. Tom suggests that he and Casy remain behind and repair the Wilson car while the others go ahead, try to get jobs, and perhaps save some money. Ma, who insists that the family must stay together, grabs a jack and threatens to fight Pa. Ma feels that all they have left in the world is their family and, once the family unit is destroyed, there will be nothing to live for. She wins the argument.

Al drives ahead with the others to find a camp site, while Tom and Casy remove the defective connecting-rod. Casy admits that he is uneasy because too many people are heading west looking for work. Tom again explains his philosophy of putting down one foot at a time. He will cross that fence when he comes to it. Al returns, reporting that the family is camped at a place for fifty cents and that Granma, who has not been feeling well since Grampa's death, is now delirious. Al gives Tom and Casy some food which Ma sent.

While Casy guards the Wilson car, Tom and Al drive the Hudson to a junk-yard to look for parts. Al tries to get Tom to talk about the prison, but Tom tells him he would rather forget it for the present. Someday, he will tell all about it. They find a used-car lot with many wrecked cars, one of which is similar to theirs. The attendant is a one-eyed man who hates his boss and therefore gives them a good price on the rod, a flashlight, and some socket wrenches. Feeling very fortunate, Al and Tom return to the Wilson car and insert the rod that very night.

When they join up with the rest of the family at the campsite, the proprietor informs them that they will have to pay an extra fifty cents if they want to stay. The fee is fifty cents a car, otherwise a deputy will arrest them as vagrants. Tom begins to argue with the man and Pa tells him to stop. Tom compromises when he tells the proprietor that he will take his car some distance down the road and sleep in the ditch, but the others will stay until morning.

A ragged man warns the Joads that some California landowners have advertised for more workers than there are jobs available. He himself has learned the hard way, having gone west and lost his wife and two children to starvation, before giving up and returning home. Pa is disturbed about this report, but Casy reminds them that what is true for one man is not true for another. Ma is still anxious to get on to California "where it's rich an' green." Tom takes Uncle John and they look for another spot to spend the night. As Tom is leaving, he throws a lump of dirt at the proprietor's wooden house. He is an angry at the man for calling him a bum.

Commentary

The unity of the group is being further menaced in this chapter, by the break-down of Wilson's Dodge, by the unfriendly camp proprietor who momentarily separates Tom and Uncle John from the family, and by Granma's deteriorating condition.

Ma makes her first strong stand as champion of the cause of family unity when she brandishes her jackhandle at Pa and flatly refuses to leave Tom and Casy behind. She knows that in their wandering all they have left is the sense of the family.

The spectre-like figure of the ragged man is a prophet of future doom. His description of the typical farm boss's hiring technique will prove accurate (in Chapter 26): "The more fellas he can get, an' the hungrier, less he's gonna pay."

In this chapter Steinbeck reinforces his conviction that ownership breeds selfish indifference to others: the one-eyed junk man detests his boss, and the camp owner is portrayed as a victimizer of itinerant "bums."

CHAPTER 17

Summary

This intercalary chapter describes the temporary worlds which are established by twenty or so families each night at the camp sites. These little communities have their leaders, laws, rules of etiquette, and rituals for establishing relationships, all of which are for the health, protection, and happiness of the people. A world is built each night, and it is torn down at daybreak.

Commentary

Though these men, women and children may break written laws and offend the authorities, they are developing an unwritten code which is both necessary and operative. Far from being 'lawless,' they punish wrongdoers instantly and they instinctively protect the weak and the sick. Just as the Joads buried Grampa without notifying the officials, so these people do the things they have to do and, in so doing, give striking evidence of their native common sense.

CHAPTER 18

Summary

The Joads move westward through the mountains and deserts of New Mexico and Arizona. Water is scarce and the price climbs to fifteen cents a gallon. They reach the bridge at Topack and realize they are in California, even though they still have a desert to cross.

They stop at a small encampment along the river at Needles. Ruthie and Winfield wade into the water. Tom decides to take a bath before he goes to sleep, and the other men follow him into the stream. They are white-skinned apart from their sunburned faces and arms, and as they scrub themselves with sand, they discuss Granma's health, the country they have just come through and the harsh desert ahead.

While they are bathing, two men — father and son — approach. They are returning from the west, going back to Texas, and they tell the Joad men a terrible story about their experiences in California. It is beautiful country, but there is no work. The land and cattle companies own everything, and deputy sherrifs keep people on the move. Pa cannot believe the story about the man who owns a million acres that he does not farm and who rides around in a bulletproof vest, afraid of dying.

They hear the word, "Okie" for the first time. "It use' ta mean you was from Oklahoma. Now it means . . . you're scum." Surely, they argue, there must be work if you are ready to do anything. The father and son, with bitter wisdom, know that nothing they say will deter the Joads from continuing their journey.

At this point Noah makes his decision to take the path of least resistance, and not to go on with the family. He loves it here beside the water and will catch fish to live. He asks Tom to tell Ma, and Tom watches his brother grow smaller as he walks away down the river.

Granma mutters and chokes, naked under a piece of pink curtain. She calls out to Grampa and nags at him as if he were still alive. Ma tells Rose of Sharon it is a comfort to know that dying and bearing children are all part of the same thing, a time of change in human life, but she knows that her daughter does not understand. A large woman, a member of the Jehovite religious sect, looks into the tent, sees Granma, and offers to have a prayer meeting for the "dear soul gonna join her Jesus." Ma refuses angrily. Rose of Sharon asks why she is so stubborn, and Ma, taking most of the strain of the family, says she just can't stand it: "I'd just fly all apart." The Jehovites have their meeting anyway, and Granma, previously agitated, goes into a deep sleep. Ma regrets that she was short-tempered with these well-meaning people.

With Granma asleep, Rose of Sharon tells Ma about Connie's plans to study electricity at nights. Suddenly, they are startled by a deputy sheriff who beats on the tarpaulin and announces that he will run them in if he finds the family still there by the same time tomorrow. Ma, her face black with anger, picks up an iron skillet and threatens him. He repeats his order to move on but, at the sight of the skillet, backs off and moves along to the next tent.

Ma finds Tom and tells him about the incident. Tom takes the opportunity to tell Ma that Noah has gone. "Family's fallin' apart," she says after a long silence, "I jus' can't seem to think no more."

They start packing to move on. They are worried about Granma, about how much pork they have and the fact that they have not had time to wash their clothes. They want the Wilsons to go with them, but Sairy is dying of cancer and will not make it across the desert. Casy comforts Sairy with a silent prayer. Ma takes two bills and some pork and leaves them on the ground, because she knows that Wilson will not take them directly.

The Joads then set off toward the desert, stopping to fill up at a service station. When they have gone the attendant remarks to his helper, "Them goddam Okies got no sense and no feeling. . . . They ain't a hell of a lot better than gorillas."

As night falls they top the pass and start to move across the black cinder desert. Uncle John confides in Casy that he feels guilty about the death of his wife. He did not get the doctor the night she died and he believes that he killed her. Casy does not offer consolation, saying only that a man's life must be his own to sort out: "A fella builds his own sins right up from the groun'." At the same time, Connie and Rose of Sharon make love surreptitiously. Ma lies beside Granma, feeling the struggling body and the sobbing breath of the old woman, who is dying.

During the night they pass an agricultural inspection station. The officer insists on searching the truck, but Ma tells him that they must get Granma to a doctor, so he lets them go on. When they do reach a gas station, Ma then claims that Granma is fine. Tom and Pa wonder why Ma is being so contradictory, and decide that she is probably tired from the trip.

All night they drive and at dawn they reach Mojave. The sun comes up behind them and they see the valley below, green and beautiful, its trees in rows and its farmhouses neatly painted. Everyone scrambles to look, and Ruthie whispers, "It's California."

Ma climbs down stiffly, her face like putty. "The fambly's here," she says and buckles at the knees. She tells them that Granma was dead before they stopped at the inspection station the previous night; she had been afraid that the family would have been stopped from going on if the dead woman had been discovered. The others are awestruck.

They have made it across the desert to California. Ma and Pa wish that Granma could have seen the pretty country. Tom thinks it would not have mattered much to the old folks. Their lives were in the past. Ruthie and Winfield are the family members whose future lies in California. They have forty dollars left, and as Tom goes on to say, "We gonna start clean! We sure ain't bringing nothin' with us."

The truck rolls down into the great valley.

Commentary

At the beginning of this chapter the Colorado River provides an ironic baptism for the Joads. There they learn the meaning of the term Okie which is to be their name in the new land. There Sairy Wilson prepares to die. There Noah, a modern Ishmael, departs to find his own Eden along the river flowing through the barren desert. And there the trooper warns the Joads to keep moving.

The family is splitting up more quickly now with the departure of Noah, the break with the Wilsons who had become a part of the family, and the death of Granma. To counteract the disintegrating process, Ma's strength seems to double. She lies with a corpse through the sleepless night so that her family can reach the Promised Land. Casy says of her in wonder, "John, there's a woman so great with love — she scares me."

CHAPTER 19

Summary

In the early days California had belonged to Mexico, but "a horde of tattered feverish Americans" had poured in with their guns and stolen the land, and made it their own. The children of these new owners lost the hunger for this land. There was no longer a "stomach-tearing lust for a rich acre and the shining blade to plow it." They became "shopkeepers of crops" and their giant farms were run like industries. They no longer lived on the land. They brought in immigrant laborers, who worked like the slaves of ancient Rome, although the landowners did not see it that way.

Then came the hordes of migrant Okies, who at first numbered 20,000, then over 300,000. These "new barbarians" wanted only two things: land and food, which to them were the same. A field left fallow was a sin, unused land a crime against the thin children.

The migrants lived on the edges of the towns in ghetto encampments that were always called "Hooverville." Their houses were made of corrugated paper that softened and washed away when the rains came. They tried growing little vegetable gardens on unused land, but a deputy sherrif would always come around and move them off for trespassing. They thought of joining forces — twenty of them protecting a piece of land with guns — but "they'd just shoot us like rats."

For some, morality changed in the camps. What was stealing? You stole a bottle of milk, or a bit of copper to sell to buy meat. That was different because the kids were hungry. The landowners never went to jail for their bigger thefts, but that was different too. "The fellas that bribed congressmen and legislatures never went to jail neither."

That is what the migrants talked about in the Hoovervilles.

They were harrassed, told to move on and burned out, and they still poured out of Kansas, Arkansas, Oklahoma, Texas and New Mexico.

The great owners were scared of them, because they knew their history and they knew that when a majority of the people are hungry and cold, they will take by force what they need. The migrants, "sharp-faced men, lean from hunger and hard from resisting it," squatted and talked in the Hoovervilles and looked at the rich land all around them. When a child died in a tent, they took up a collection and prayed for each other.

Commentary

In this intercalary chapter Steinbeck again gives proof of the broadness of vision which makes his novels valid social and historical documents. While he tends to be somewhat simplistic in extolling the virtues of the poor as opposed to the vices of the rich, his is not simply a black and white world. The rich landowners in this chapter are as much the victims of circumstances as the hungry migrants. Their ancestors who wrested the land from the Mexicans were just as desperate as the Okies are now. But possession and a soft life have weakened the landowners, and they will succumb to success just as surely as the Okies will rise from their failures.

CHAPTER 20

Summary

The Joads arrive in Bakersfield and bury Granma. It was not the nice funeral she had wanted, but it was all they could afford. They decide to camp until they get work, and find their first Hooverville at the edge of town, a slovenly collection of tents, cars and shacks.

Tom strikes up a conversation with a young man, Floyd Knowles, who is grinding the valves on his old Buick. When Tom asks about work Floyd responds, "Lookin' for work? What ya think ever'body else is lookin' for? Di'monds?" There is no work available. Tom finds this hard to believe and they begin to talk.

Floyd has seen the handbills and so have all the other migrants. The handbills have lured so many workers out to California, that the owners of the fruit ranches do not have to pay high wages. There is work sometimes, Floyd explains: a large peach orchard that employs only nine men year 'round hires 3,000 men for two weeks at picking time. Tom wonders why the workers do not organize. It has been tried, Floyd tells him, and the organizers were put on a blacklist and were never able to work again. If a migrant caused too much trouble, he would end up as "one little line in the paper — vagrant foun' dead." The best way to stay out of trouble is to pretend to be "bull-simple." Let the police think you are dumb.

Back at the Joad tent, a number of silent, hungry children watch Ma make stew. Tom and Casy talk. Casy, still thinking and watching people, says he now can "hear the way folks are feelin'." He wants to do something to help make their miserable lives better. Tom, more practical than Casy, remarks that "prayer never brought in no side-meat." When he was in prison, though, he developed a sense for when trouble was coming, and he feels it in this camp.

Rose of Sharon and Connie have an argument. He wishes he had stayed home studying tractors, rather than coming west; life seems hard to him in the camp. She berates him because she wants to have a house before the baby is born, and she is afraid he is giving up.

The children continue to watch Ma cook the stew. One small boy claims to have eaten already, but an older girl, who offers to help with the fire, says he is always bragging. The girl tells Ma about a government camp where her family once lived. There were toilets, hot water, dances on Saturday night and no mean "cops."

Meanwhile, drawn to the Buick by his love of cars, Al meets Floyd. Al is interested in girls, but Floyd is married with a family and he talks about how tired he is from looking for enough work to keep them fed.

Ma is worried by the children clustered around the stew pot: she has her own family to feed. Sadly, she decides that they have to eat inside the tent, but she will leave some stew in the bottom of the pot for the children to share. Later that evening, an angry, unhappy woman comes complaining to Ma that she should mind her own business. The woman's child had had some of the Joad's stew and had come home asking his mother why their family had none. Ma tries to explain that she could not turn away a child with hungry eyes, but the woman storms away.

Al comes back very excited. In return for help with the car, Floyd has told him that there is work up north in the Santa Clara valley, which is two hundred miles away. Tom thinks this is too far, but Floyd says he will soon learn that you have to take what can be found. Al decides he wants to go anyway, even if the family does not like it.

Two cars loaded with discouraged men who have been looking for work arrive back in the camp, and Floyd, Al and Tom do not need to ask them whether they have had any luck.

A new Chevrolet drives up. A man steps out and announces that he is a contractor hiring men for work in Tulare County. He claims to be paying about thirty cents. Floyd begins to argue with him. He wants the contractor to write out the amount he intends to pay, because he is afraid the employer will get many more men than he really needs and will finally have to pay only fifteen cents an hour. The men will accept it because they are hungry. The contractor shouts in the direction of the Chevrolet, and out steps Joe, a deputy sheriff wearing a star, riding breeches and a pistol at his waist. The deputy tells Floyd to get in the car. He threatens the other men that if they do not get out of this camp and work in Tulare, he might enforce his orders from the Board of Health to burn the camp.

Floyd hits the deputy and dashes away down the line of tents. The sherrif staggers as Tom trips him, reaches for his gun and fires at Floyd. He misses him and hits a woman in front of a tent, tearing off her hand. At this moment The Reverend Casy steps out of the group of men and kicks the deputy unconscious. Casy tells Tom to leave because he has broken parole. The siren screams as a police car arrives carrying four men armed with rifles.

The deputy, dazed, does not recognize Casy. But Casy states that he was the man who knocked him out. He asks the deputies to see how badly the woman's hand is hurt. The leader goes off to look and, returning, says almost with pride: "Jesus, what a mess a .45 does make!" The deputies leave with Casy between them.

Later in the evening, the family gathers by the fire. Uncle John, still experiencing his self-induced guilt, has reached the point where he has to get drunk. Ma and Pa understand why he has to do this. Rose of Sharon is wondering where Connie has gotten to; he seems to have gone. Pa comments that he was no good anyway, and that the family is well rid of him.

Floyd warns Tom and Al that they should leave the camp. The deputy will have arranged revenge and "pool-room boys" will be coming that night to burn down the camp. Tom returns and explains to Ma that they have to leave. He cannot afford to be taken by the police. He finds Uncle John drunk by the river, and knocks him out so he can bring him along. Rose of Sharon says she wants to stay and wait for Connie, but Tom and Ma persuade her to come along. Once again they pack up to move.

Ma is worried about Tom. The family is breaking up, and she is afraid he is going to lose his temper and get into trouble. He explains his feeling about the deputies; burning down the camp is not within the law. They are attacking the pride of the migrants, and Tom says there "comes a time when the on'y way a fella can keep his decency is by takin' a sock at a cop."

At the gate to the camp they are stopped by a crowd of men with pick handles and shotguns. They are the people who have been brought in to burn the camp. Tom stiffens, but he puts on a servile whine and asks them for directions to Tulare. He stops the car some distance away and looks back to see what is going on. He tells Ma that he has decided to go south and look for better surroundings in the government camp they have been told about.

Ma is proud of him for using his self-control to help the family get safely out of the camp. She advises her son to have patience. These problems will not destroy them. "Why", says Ma, "we're the people — we go on." Tom says he has never heard her talk so much in his life; she says there never was so much reason to.

Tom turns the truck south and starts to drive into the darkness.

Commentary

This chapter is the longest and most melodramatic in the novel thus far. It begins in despair with the Joads unable to scrape up enough money to give Granma a decent burial; it continues in frustration as the Joads gradually realize that misery is almost as rampant in California as it was back in Oklahoma, the little man still being victimized by the whole socio-economic system; it gives way to violence when Tom and Casy encounter the deputy and again when the mob razes Hooverville; and finally, there is the relief of escape when the Joads escape the doomed camp and head for the government establishment at Weedpatch.

Strong contrast is provided in the desertion of Rose of Sharon by her husband Connie and Jim Casy's self-sacrifice for Tom.

Thus far the family has lost its dog, Grampa, Noah, Granma, Casy and Connie. However, though the family is disintegrating as a single unit, it is being replaced by a larger concept, one advocated earlier by Casy. The people will continue because they will help each other. Al helps Floyd grind his car valves, and Floyd, in turn, tells Al where there might be work. And as Ma is cooking her meager meal, she cannot help sharing a little with the starving children around her.

These examples of spontaneous generosity are all part of a naturalistic determinism which pervades this chapter as it does the whole novel. Various people are constantly doing things because their peculiar nature or circumstances prevent them from acting otherwise. Thus, even though Floyd has warned Tom to act stupid because the authorities arrest any potential Hooverville leaders, Floyd himself questions the labor contractor so closely that the deputy tries to arrest him as a "red." Casy offers himself so spontaneously as a scape-goat that Uncle John is moved to getting drunk. And Tom shows signs of his basically violent nature when he trips one deputy and wants to attack another with a jack handle. Ma alone retains an almost regal patience throughout the turmoil. Though her primary goal is to preserve her own family, she sees beyond it. She knows that they are only one small group in a wave of humanity which will ultimately prevail against all obstacles.

CHAPTER 21

Summary

The migrants are becoming desperate. A simple, agrarian people unaccustomed to machines, they are baffled by the ways of industry. They gradually become hostile as they see their children grow hungrier, and the little western towns, sensing the hostility of these ragged strangers, begin to arm themselves as though to repel an invader.

The western landowners feel panic and terror for their property. They try to convince themselves that they are good and the invaders bad by saying that the "goddamned Okies" are a dirty, ignorant, degenerate people with no sense of property rights. While the owners band together, hire agents, spies and blacklisters, the big farmers squeeze out the small farmers who become migrants themselves.

Commentary

This intercalary chapter, like 19 and 25, is a lesson in California land ownership and the dangers inherent in the 'laissez-faire' aspects of free enterprise in a capitalistic system. The law of supply and demand can be used against the little man by an organization big enough to control one segment of the economy.

CHAPTER 22

Summary

The Joads drive to the government camp near Weedpatch, where there is a vacancy for one family. Ma is thrilled to learn that there are wash tubs in the camp. Tom registers at the camp office while the rest of the family unload and prepare for sleep. When the watchman informs Tom that no police are allowed in the camp unless they have a warrant, and mentions that the camp is governed by campers who have been elected by their peers, Tom can hardly believe it. He becomes even more excited when he finds out that dances are held every Saturday night. Ma is the only one awake in the Joad camp when Tom returns. Tom tells her that the camp is nice. In the morning, he promises, he'll tell her everything he has found out about it.

Tom is woken early the next day by the sound of iron hitting iron.

He follows the sound until he sees a girl working over a hot stove. Two men emerge from a tent, and the eldest asks Tom to have breakfast with them. After breakfast, the two men, Mr. Wallace and his son, Wilkie, tell Tom that they have been working for the past twelve days laying pipe for Mr. Thomas, a local farmer. They invite him to go to work with them, and Tom cannot understand why they would share their good fortune. He tells Ruthie where he is going, and merrily joins the Wallaces as they walk off to work.

Mr. Thomas informs them that he has been forced by the Farmer's Association, under the threat of foreclosure, to reduce the men's hourly rate from 30¢ to 25¢ an hour. He also warns the three men that the authorities are planning to create a disturbance at the next Saturday night dance in order to have an excuse to raid and close the government camp. The local authorities believe that the government camps are spoiling the migrants and if the Okies stay in one place too long, they will organize and demand decent wages. Since someone who demands a fair wage is labelled a "red," Tom decides that he must be a "red" himself.

Ruthie and Winfield investigate the camp toilets, and they think they have broken one after it flushes. Scared, they run back to Ma. Ma accompanies the children back to the toilets, and a man enters and abruptly tells her that the "Ladies" is on the other side. He then explains, in a friendlier tone of voice, that the ladies' committee will be calling on her shortly.

Ma returns to the tent, wakes up everyone, and tries to finish with breakfast before the visit. Jim Rawley, the camp manager, strolls by and has a cup of coffee with Ma. Ma is almost moved to tears when she realizes she is back among her own type of people.

The Joads eat fast and the men take the truck to look for work. Rose of Sharon takes a shower in the wonderful camp facilities and Ma decides she will take one too. While Ma is gone, a religious fanatic comes by on her way to the laundry. The woman sees that Rose of Sharon is pregnant and she begins to criticize moral conduct in the camp. The woman describes a recent bloody stillbirth which she blames on playacting and immodest dancing in the camp. When she leaves, Rawley returns and he tries to reassure Rose of Sharon by telling her that the woman is a troublesome fanatic. The only 'sins' in camp which cause stillbirth, says Rawley, are cold and hunger and overwork.

Meanwhile, Pa, Uncle John, and Al are driving around the area looking for work. The country is dotted with signs which say "No Help Wanted. No Trespassing." They pick up another man from the camp who tells them that he has searched for work all week with no luck. They decide to return to camp and save gasoline.

The welcoming committee leaves Ma feeling wonderfully optimistic, and she begins to make plans for the future, hoping that the men have found work. Mrs. Sandry, the religious fanatic, returns and again begins to criticize the evil people in the camp who persist in dancing and hugging. Ma disagrees with the woman, orders her away, and threatens her with a piece of wood. Mrs. Sandry suddenly throws a fit and begins to howl. Rawley arrives and asks some people to get Mrs. Sandry to her tent. Rawley asks Ma to be more tolerant towards the wretched woman who is not well, but Rose of Sharon remains convinced that the fanatic's predictions may somehow come true. Ma comforts Rose of Sharon but is saddened herself when Pa returns and has found no work.

Commentary

This chapter contrasts sharply with the preceding one. At Hooverville, the Joads had been met by a "bull-simple" migrant; but here they are respectfully greeted by the watchman. The new camp is clean and well organized, and the committee that runs it inspires confidence and hope in the people — unlike the dread the people felt toward the cops at Hooverville.

Although by contrast the government camp seems like paradise, it is not. Tom is the only member of the family to find work, and even that is temporary. Rose of Sharon is very apprehensive about her unborn baby, especially after the encounter with the religious fanatic. The government camp is an island of relief for its many campers, but it is not the realization of their dreams.

CHAPTER 23

Summary

The migrant people were hungry for everything, including amusement. They told jokes and some excelled at captivating audiences with vivid tales of the Indian wars. Others would go to a movie, come home and give a detailed re-run of the entire plot to anyone who cared to listen. With a little money, a man could get drunk and dream of the good old times while communing with nature. And some played harmonicas or guitars or fiddles while the people clapped and danced. Through it all the preacher preached and baptized, hurling his grovelling converts into the saving waters.

Commentary

In this charming little chapter, Steinbeck suggests that the Okies are the type of people who provide the stuff of great folk epics and folk music.

CHAPTER 24

Summary

On Saturday, the government camp is a hive of activity as the campers prepare themselves for the dance that evening. The Chairman of the Central Committee, Ezra Huston, holds a meeting in order to plan strategy for the prevention of violence expected that evening. The Chairman of the Entertainment Committee, Willie Eaton, tells the meeting that he has twenty strong boys who, at the first sign of trouble, will surround the instigators and, without bloodshed, force them to leave. By doing so, any excuse for the authorities to raid the camp will be eliminated.

As the cars of guests begin to arrive at the gate, each guest must mention the name of the camper who has invited them. The guests consist of local farmers and their families, and migrants from other camps.

At the Joad camp, Ruthie and Winfield eat their food quickly and run off to join the other children around the band's platform. Al also eats quickly, but he then spends a half hour shaving. He is hoping to meet some pretty girls at the dance. Pa and Uncle John go off to talk to some people about getting work. Rose of Sharon blushes with embarrassment when Tom tells her that she is getting prettier, but that she is also growing larger. Ma is pleased to learn that Tom is already on a committee. She thinks Tom was appointed to a committee because he has a job, not knowing that he is part of the group organized to maintain order. Tom is told by Willie Eaton that he and an Indian named Jule Vitela will be watching the front gate. He and Jule are to check the guests as they come in.

Three men are spotted by Jule as they nervously walk through the gate. They tell the guard that the Jacksons have invited them. When asked, Jackson tells the committee that he worked with the three men, but he did not invite them. It is decided that the three men should be left alone, but watched very closely. A young boy tells Huston that there is a police car with six men in it parked just down the road.

The dance is in full swing and all goes smoothly for quite a while. Then, one of the three suspected men insists on dancing with a particular girl. He is quickly surrounded by members of Entertainment Committee, as are his two companions. The three men are given a severe reprimand for their shameful action against their own people and warned of the consequences of any future trouble. After their rebuking, the three men are allowed to go. At the first hint of a fight, a carload of deputies arrives at the gate. But the guard tells them that there isn't any trouble, forcing the deputies to withdraw.

Later on in the evening, a migrant named Black Hat, tells a story about the mountain people who were hired as cheap labor in Akron, and how they joined a union. The locals began arming themselves against the "reds" in their town. One Sunday, five thousand mountain men walked up and down the street shooting their guns in the air in a "Turkey Shoot." There hasn't been any trouble in Akron since. Black Hat suggests that the men of the Hoovervilles go on their own "Turkey Shoot."

Commentary

Tension mounts in this chapter despite the courageous attempts of the migrants to organize their camp and prevent trouble at the dance. Paradoxically, it is precisely their ability to govern themselves and cope with such situations that arouses the fear of the landowners and the deputies. If left unchecked, these migrant hoards might organize throughout California and fight for social change.

CHAPTER 25

Summary

In spring, California is a paradise of fruit blossoms and tender vegetable plants. Gradually the country becomes heavy with produce, the result of scientific research and intensive cultivation. But when harvest time approaches, the big canneries, owned by the big landowners, depress prices and force wholesale crop dumping even though people are starving everywhere. Small farmers are ruined. And so it is, that "Men who have created new fruits in the world cannot create a system whereby their fruits may be eaten."

People try to net the potatoes thrown into the river, but guards hold them back. They come in cars to get the dumped oranges, but the fruit is sprayed with kerosene and burned. Pigs are slaughtered in ditches and buried in quicklime. And children die of malnutrition. While failure hangs over the State like a great sorrow, there is a growing wrath in the eyes of the hungry. And, in the souls of the people "the grapes of wrath are filling and growing heavy, growing heavy for the vintage."

Commentary

This interchapter concludes the first half (Chapters 19-25) of the California section of the novel (Chapters 19-30). The land is indeed as fertile as the Joads had dreamed it might be. But men have not devised ways of sharing nature's abundance, and tons of food are destroyed while people starve. Steinbeck sums up the resentment, frustration and anger dwelling in the hearts and souls of the people under the dominant Biblical image of "grapes of wrath." There is a strong implication that the wrath about to be visited on man is the very wrath of God, who will no longer permit such grave social injustices.

CHAPTER 26

Summary

After spending a month in the government camp at Weedpatch, the Joads have no work and are almost out of food. Ma insists that they have a meeting and discuss the situation. Pa hates to leave the camp, but Ma observes ironically that they can't eat "niceness." Moreover,

Winfield is sick and Rose of Sharon is almost due to have her baby. They must move out to seek work elsewhere. It is finally decided that they will leave in the morning. Everyone begins to prepare for their departure.

Meanwhile Al goes to call on a girl friend to say goodbye. The girl is annoyed at the news and suggests that they should marry. When Al learns that she is not pregnant he trips her and they roll in the grass. Al promises that he will make some money and return in about a month's time. Tom, Willie Eaton and Jule Vitela talk about forming a union to protect the workers and keep wages at a decent level. Pa and Uncle John use the flush toilets one last time and Uncle John confesses that he is doing some sinful thinking. Pa finds such sin commendable in that "It's a whole hell of a lot cheaper."

It is still dark when Ma rouses everyone. They eat some cold biscuits, load and leave, heading toward Bakersfield. The truck has a flat tire and, while they are repairing it, a pleasant looking man drives up and tells them there is work forty miles north at the Hooper ranch. The man asks the Joads whether they know of other people looking for work, and Tom directs him to the Weedpatch camp. Ma begins making unrealistic plans again, hoping for a little house and a steady supply of food.

When they arrive at the ranch they are escorted by four policemen on motorcycles, past a crowd of jeering fist-waving people, to the shabby fruitpickers' camp.

Soon the Joads are busy picking peaches at five cents a box. In spite of being warned, Tom hurriedly picks a box, bruising each peach as he dumps them out of the bucket. He is refused credit because of the damaged fruit. He goes back out into the orchard and tells his family that their fruit won't be accepted and that they all have to start over again, only working much more slowly. Soon the entire family, except for Rose of Sharon, is picking in the orchard, and by nightfall they have earned a dollar. Ma takes the credit slip to the camp store to buy groceries. She quickly discovers that the food prices are higher than in the town store. With the dollar spent, she still doesn't have enough to feed the family. The timid shopkeeper breaks the rules by loaning Ma ten cents for sugar. Ma then goes straight to the Joad hut and cooks supper.

Afterwards, Tom decides that he is going to see what the trouble was outside the fence. Pa is too tired to do anything and Al wants to go looking for a girl. Tom heads for the gate, but is turned back by the guard, so he circles and crosses the fence at another point. He soon encounters a group of agitators led by the preacher, Jim Casy. Tom and Jim are very pleased to see each other again, and the preacher tells Tom of his experiences in jail, especially the sour bean incident when the prisoners were given better food after presenting a united front. Casy warns Tom that when the deputies rout the strikers, the workers in the camp will be picking peaches for two and a half cents a box. Tom does not feel that warning the people will do any good, because, like the Joads, they must have food, regardless of labor movements. Casy praises labor leaders for their spirit of self-sacrifice.

Suddenly, they hear men approaching, and realize that the deputies are after them. They try to escape, but Jim and Tom are stopped. Casy tries to appeal to the deputies' higher nature when he says: "You don't know what you're a-doin. You're helpin' to starve kids." But, just as he says these words, a man strikes him with a pick handle crushing his head. Enraged, Tom wrenches the pick handle from the deputy and deals him several blows which prove to be fatal. A second policeman manages to strike Tom, smashing his nose and gashing his face, but Tom is able to escape, hide in some brush, and gradually work his way back to the house where the Joads are sleeping. He shivers through a sleepless night.

At dawn, Ma rises early, sends Pa for a little food, and then notices Tom's condition. Tom tells his story to the whole family. He wants to leave because, with everyone looking for the man who attacked the deputy, he is a real threat to the family. Ma will not allow Tom to leave, insisting that he needs protection and that the members of his family are the only people he can trust. Ma feeds them all, sends them out to pick peaches, and hides Tom. When Tom tells her Casy's last words, she forgives him for his violence.

When Pa brings the news that Tom's victim is dead, Ma decides they will smuggle him from the ranch between mattresses on the truck bed. They leave, getting a little gas in exchange for a work slip, then drive north along back roads until they happen to see an advertisement for cotton pickers. Tom convinces the family that they should hire on at the field where he hides in a nearby weedy culvert until his face heals.

Commentary

This longest of all chapters in the whole novel begins with Ma assuming leadership and forcing the frustrated men to take action. She knows that this is dangerous, because the men can lose all initiative when a woman assumes command. But she also knows that if they remain any longer in the government camp, they are doomed.

Again, after Tom has killed the deputy, Ma is the one who decides that they must leave camp and hide Tom. Pa is incapable of facing such a great decision, and Ma forges ahead even though, in doing so, she knows she is usurping Pa's leadership. She tells Tom sadly: "Pa's lost his place. He ain't the head no more . . . There ain't no fambly now."

Still, as the Joad family crumbles, there are faint signs of a greater sense of brotherhood emerging. Before his brutal death Casy, like Christ, reminds his tormentors that they don't know what they are doing. And this is very true, for the deputies are as much the victims of the blind socio-economic forces as the Okies they are persecuting. In trying to organize labor, Casy is doing the only thing he possibly can to help the people. He knows that they will be maltreated until they meet the economic squeeze with a greater force, the force that comes with a united front. Tom is beginning to grasp the basic ideas of organized protest, but he must give the matter much more thought before he is ready to continue and complete Casy's mission.

CHAPTER 27

Summary

Cotton pickers are wanted and the signs go up along the roads. A worker who does not have his own bag must buy one for a dollar, and he gets 80 cents for every hundred pounds of cotton he picks. He must keep a record each time he has his sack weighed, or he is likely to be cheated. To balance the crooked scales, he slips a few rocks or clods into each load.

Again, there are too many workers, and a field which would have provided steady work for fifty pickers is swarmed over by five hundred so that the job is soon finished. Whole families work all day for a few pounds of side-meat. And winter is coming.

Commentary

The Joads, like the other migrants, are hoping to find steady work picking cotton. This chapter prepares us for their disappointment. Even when the farmer pays a half decent wage there is only a short respite from hunger, because there are too many laborers for the harvest and the work is soon finished.

CHAPTER 28

Summary

Twelve box cars stand end to end beside the stream. The Joads are living in one end of a car, and it is nicer than anything since the government camp. The Wainwrights live at the other end, beyond a piece of curtain. One Saturday they drive into Tulare and buy a tin stove, new overalls for the men and a dress for Ma.

In the evening they go to the crossroads store and compare notes with the other cotton pickers. Ma buys meat and milk for Rose of Sharon. She lets Pa buy a can of syrup for hot cakes. Ruthie and Winfield get a large box of Cracker Jacks each, because Pa says they had worked hard that day.

Back at camp, Ma is cooking supper when Winfield rushes in to tell her that Ruthie has told about Tom in a childish argument with a bigger girl over sharing her Cracker Jacks. Ruthie said her brother could kill the other girl's brother, as he had killed someone before. Ma sets out to find Tom, taking some pork chops and fried potatoes for him. Tom is hiding in a cave which is among some wild blackberry bushes. While he eats in the pitch dark, Ma tells him what Ruthie has done. Tom is not worried; it was just kid's talk.

He will have a bad scar and his nose will be crooked, but his face is healing well. He thinks that may be a good thing, since he will not be recognized. Ma wants him to go away and says that he is to have the seven dollars she has been saving. He does not want to take the money, but he says that he has known from the start that he would have to leave.

He starts to talk about Casy. Even though he was not conscious of it at the time, he has found himself remembering things that Casy said, how a man did not have a soul of his own, but only a small piece of a great big soul. "Woe to him that is alone when he falleth, for he hath not another to help him up." Tom says that most preaching is about the poor, but he remembers the government camp where they helped themselves and each other and settled disputes without the need for the hated police. He would like to try the same thing again. He wants to do what Casy did. Even if they kill him, Tom says mystically, he will be around everywhere.

> Wherever they's a fight so hungry people can eat, I'll be there. Wherever they's a cop beatin' up a guy, I'll be there . . . I'll be in the way guys yell when they're mad an' — I'll be in the way kids laugh when they're hungry and they know supper's ready. An' when our folks eat the stuff they raise an' live in the houses they build — why, I'll be there.

In the black of the cave, he agrees to take the money and go. He guides his mother out, and although her eyes are wet, she does not cry.

On the way back a man stops her and tells her that he is a small producer of cotton who needs pickers. After asking about wages, Ma agrees that the family will be along early in the morning. Back at the camp she invites the Wainwrights to come too.

Mr. Wainwright is worried about Aggie, who is out with Al every night. Both families understand the situation and Ma says that either she or Pa will speak to Al. She tells Pa and Uncle John that she found Tom and sent him away. Ma essentially is becoming the head of the family. Pa no longer cares much, but finds it "funny! Women takin' over the fambly." "Woman", Ma tells him, "got all her life in her arms. Man got it all in his head." Men need things like farms and work, but for women life is like a river. "People is goin' on — changin' a little, maybe, but goin' right on."

Al comes in and announces that he and Aggie want to get married. He is surprised when Ma tells him how happy they are, but not pleased when she asks him to stay until spring because they need him. Ma puts on some coffee and starts to make pancakes, Mrs. Wainwright brings some sugar, and the two families have a celebration.

Rose of Sharon leaves the party and walks toward the stream and the trail beside it. She hides deep in the bush and the next morning she insists on going to pick cotton.

They set off early because there are only twenty acres to be picked and they want the work. When they get there they are not the first. The owner signs them in by name on a list against which he will later tally what they have picked. The line of pickers moves out across the field and by eleven the work is done. Disconsolately the pickers cluster back to the barnyard to be paid their meagre wages.

Al drives back, but Rose of Sharon starts to shiver violently. The baby is not due yet, but she is not well. They put her feet in hot water, rub them, and Mrs. Wainwright offers painkillers and salts.

It starts to rain. The men have been gathering wood, and Ma sends them out again and again for more. She finally lets them stop for dry overalls and hot coffee. Evening comes early, as the families huddle together in the boxcar listening to the rain pouring down on the roof.

Commentary

This chapter begins on an optimistic tone with the Joads finding work and decent shelter. Their short-lived respite begins to fade when, as a result of Ruthie's bragging, Tom is forced to hide in the hole by the culvert. This is an ironical twist of fate in that Tom refused adamantly (in Chapter 6) to enter the cave which Muley Graves offered to share with him. Tom can no longer afford to be proud, he is entirely dispossessed. The cave sequence may also be seen as a "return-to-the-womb" image suggesting Tom's rebirth. Tom's earlier egotism gives way to a devotion to the family. Now, Tom is ready to help all men. He will be Casy's most ardent disciple.

Again, as the Joads reach out to encompass a larger segment of mankind, they themselves continue to dissolve as a family unit. Tom must flee, Al is thinking mainly of his future with Aggie, and Pa and Uncle John feel that they are losing their interest in living along with any control they once enjoyed over the family.

CHAPTER 29

Summary

The clouds form and the rain begins — slowly at first, then a steady downpour. Gradually the creeks and rivers flow over their banks flooding the migrants' tents and stalling their old cars. The people move to higher ground, huddling pitifully together in barns.

There is no more work, and the migrants are not eligible for relief because they have not resided long enough in the State. Desperate with hunger and sickness, frantic men steal squawking chickens and do not even bother to run when shot at. The native citizens first pity the migrants, then grow angry at them, and finally fear them. The sheriffs swear in more deputies. When the rain finally stops and pale green grass appears, the women watch their men anxiously to see whether they have finally given up. They feel reassured when they see the men grow angry, for they know that "the break would never come so long as fear could turn to wrath."

Commentary

The last intercalary chapter contains elements of despair and hope. The migrants are terrified by the floods which bring death to many. But the same rain causes green grass to sprout up, and this symbolic resurrection suggests that the people, in whom Ma has unlimited faith, will go on.

This chapter also helps to unify the novel by linking up with Chapter 1, in which the women watch the men and are relieved to see that they do not despair. Neither the droughts of Oklahoma nor the floods of California can overcome the determination of these people.

CHAPTER 30

Summary

The rain continues. The Joads and the Wainwrights become one family when Al takes down the tarpaulin separating the families, and uses it to cover the truck's engine. In spite of the rising water, the families refuse to leave because the boxcar is sealed and dry. Rose of Sharon suffers from a cold and high fever. Pa decides to try to find some men to help him build a dike in order to keep the water at bay.

After Rose of Sharon goes into labor, Pa tells the other men that a dam must be built because his daughter is going to have a baby. The men work frantically, with mud up to their knees, to try and stem the rising water. They almost succeed, but a floating tree rams the dike and knocks a huge hole in it. In an instant, the entire flood wall is washed away, and the area is swamped with rushing water. Al desperately tries to start the truck, but the battery is dead and the vehicle is soon deeply submerged in water.

In the meantime, Ma and Mrs. Wainwright are helping Rose of Sharon through an obviously painful delivery. When Pa returns after failing to stop the rising water, he is shown a "blue shriveled little mummy," Rose of Sharon's stillborn baby. The Joad men build a platform mid-way up the boxcar in order to keep themselves and their belongings dry. Uncle John is asked to bury the dead baby, and in spite of his protests, he takes it out and floats it in an apple box down the flooded valley.

On the second day of huddling on the platform, Pa wades out into the water and returns with ten potatoes. After this last "meal", they have nothing left to eat. The next morning, Ma angrily decides that it is time for the family to leave. Al says that he is staying with Aggie, but he promises to watch after their belongings. Pa carries Rose of Sharon on his back, Ma carries Winfield and Uncle John, Ruthie. They struggle through the flood water to reach the road. Once on high ground, they make for a barn that looks dry.

Inside the barn, they see a middle-aged man and his son. The man is close to death, having given the last of his food to his boy. He will die unless he is given some liquid nourishment. Ma turns to Rose of Sharon who smiles and simply says, "Yes." Rose of Sharon asks everyone to leave her and the man alone. She then lies down beside the starving man and gently takes his head and guides it toward her full breasts.

Commentary

Though Steinbeck's conclusion might be a source of embarrassment to readers of delicate sensibility, his intention is obvious: he wanted to end with a powerful symbol of human life persisting despite the hostility of social forms and of the natural elements. Rose of Sharon transcends her own personal tragedy and reaches out in a burst of compassion which knows no barriers. Her heroic gesture is a concrete expression of Casy's philosophy twice voiced by Ma when she says, "We'll do what we got to do", and "Use'ta be the fambly was fust. It ain't so now. It's anybody."

CHARACTER SKETCHES

The following provides an analysis of the main characters in the novel. While certain minor characters, such as Mae and Al the hamburger stand owners, provide the reader with valuable insights into the various types of people encountered by the migrants in their travels, they are not included here since they do not contribute substantially to the plot or dramatic structure of the novel.

Casy, Jim

Though Jim Casy is continually reminding people that he is no longer a preacher, he nevertheless expresses, in common words, the main message of the novel — the need for social action based on the brotherhood of man. After his period of meditation in the wilderness, Casy abandons his beliefs in the personal conversion aspect of Christianity with its emphasis on the intermediary roles of Christ and the Spirit and opts rather for a half-evolved Emersonian doctrine of the Oversoul. In this view, man's soul is but a part of a greater, more universal soul, or Oversoul, to which it will be reunited in the after-life. From this insight Casy proceeds to reason that if all men have souls which are part of the one great soul, then all men are good, since they come from the same good source and will return there. And, Casy argues, if all men are good then their actions must be good — eating, drinking, talking, fornicating, cussing, and all things are holy, because they are done by man and man himself is holy. Thus it is that Casy is finally able to understand how he could have sinned so soon after performing baptisms, and with young women who were still apparently possessed by the Spirit.

While Casy's ethical relativism may be somewhat disturbing, he is most moving in his attempt to articulate the sense of universal love he feels within himself. Again, though Casy is often accused of talking too much, he is ready to act when the time comes.

He helps the Joads in their difficult journey west, allows himself to be arrested to save Tom and, finally, goes to his death with the stinging rebuke which sums up the whole human tragedy: ''You fellas don' know what you're doin'. You're helpin' to starve kids.''

Joad, Al

The sixteen-year-old son of Pa and Ma Joad. He admires and sometimes imitates his older brother Tom, but he lacks the latter's seriousness. Our first view of Al is of him swaggering home after ''tom-cattin'' all night. Girls and cars are Al's two main interests, and he never really develops any wider outlook on life. Tom realizes this when he tells Casy that Al would not quit work for the sake of a strike.

Though Al is proud to drive the family Hudson west, he is anxious to break away from the family and find work in a garage. He finally does leave the other Joads and stays with Aggie Wainwright, whom he wants to marry.

Joad, Grampa (William James Joad, ''Will'')

Grampa, the honorary head of the Joad family, is an earthy, vulgar, cantankerous old man. When he is not bragging about some youthful exploit, he is arguing about religion with Granma. He uses foul language, delights in shockingly lewd suggestions, fumbles with his pants, scratches, and dreams of going to California where he can revel in grapes. However, when the times comes to set out for California, he categorically refuses to leave Oklahoma and has to be doped and carried unconscious to the truck. Once uprooted from the land of his ancestors, Grampa soon dies and is buried by his impoverished family in a field near the road west of Oklahoma city.

Joad, Granma

Granma resembles Grampa in many ways. She has a fierce temper and is almost as vulgar in her religiosity as Grampa is in his blatant hedonism. Granma's religion is that curious mixture of revivalist doctrine and superstition which Casy abandons. She interjects 'Amens' into Casy's long prayers as a simple matter of conditioned reflex, and she seizes on the least opportunity to try to arouse that old religious feeling. Her peculiar brand of militant faith is perhaps best summed up in her command to Casy when the preacher won't pray during Grampa's fatal stroke: ''Pray, Goddam you!''

Shortly after her husband's death, Granma becomes delirious. She survives in the twilight state until the Joads reach eastern California, then dies during the night lying in the truck beside Ma.

Joad, Uncle John

Pa Joad's fifty year old brother, John is usually quiet, withdrawn and hard-working. Years ago he was married to a young girl whom he loved dearly. She was in her fourth month of pregnancy when she developed severe pains in her stomach. When she asked Uncle John to get a doctor, he told her she had "et too much". By the next day, his wife was dead of a ruptured appendix, and since that time Uncle John has felt guilty and tried to make amends by giving away almost any material goods he managed to accumulate. Now and then, overpowered by his sense of sin, he goes on violent binges with liquor and women.

Though Uncle John goes west with the rest of the family, one feels that his heart is not in it. He does not seem to hope for a brighter future but more or less accepts things the way they are even when the family is forced to live like animals.

He is obviously very angry when he sets the shrivelled corpse of Rose of Sharon's baby afloat with the words: "Go down an' tell 'em. Go down in the street and rot and tell 'em that way. . . ." But Uncle John is not a fighter, and even if he were, the odds are overwhelming. All he can do is withdraw into a state of semi-awareness as he confides in Ma that he feels half asleep most of the time.

Joad, Ma

Ma is the strong woman of Proverbs. Her control and kindness are mirrored in her face, and her eyes have that serene look of one who has somehow passed beyond suffering and pain. Nothing disturbs Ma, at least outwardly, because she knows that the whole family looks to her for guidance and stability.

In many ways, Ma embodies the philosophy of Jim Casy. She treats all creatures with the respect due to them and, while always putting the needs of her own family first, she willingly helps other people when she can. She comforts the Wilsons, shares food with the starving Hooverville children, and finds work for the Wainwrights.

Ma holds the family together as long as is humanly possible. She suffers greatly when she sees Grampa die, then Noah leave, then Granma die, and then Tom forced to hide and finally go away. But she hides her grief, knowing full well that Pa and the children could know hurt and fear only if she acknowledged hurt and fear.

Ma understands the individual needs of each member of the family. She knows that if Pa is ever defeated completely, the family will collapse. So, at times, she goads Pa into near frenzy, knowing that his anger will make him stronger by strengthening his resolve. She knows how Rose of Sharon is troubled by her pregnancy, and she threatens to slap her at times when she begins to feel too sorry for herself, but she is always ready to comfort the poor girl when the need arises. She knows that she can rely on Tom, but not on Al who lacks Tom's sense of responsibility. She understands Uncle John's need to overindulge now and then and does not criticize him for it.

As long as the family or some part of the family is together, Ma will see to it that they survive. She feels instinctively that they are the people, that they are the ones who will endure and populate the world. Though she speaks rarely, Ma expresses one of the most comprehensive morals of the novel: "If you're in trouble or hurt or need — go to poor people. They're the only ones that'll help — the only ones."

Joad, Noah

Noah, the oldest of the Joad children, is a strange, slightly misshapen young man. Though he is physically present in most of the early chapters, he remains silent and withdrawn. He is a steady worker and seems reliable, but he also seems to be aware that he is not loved like the other children. When the Joads reach the Colorado River, Noah seems captivated by the cool waters, and he decides to stay right there fishing and sitting in the sun. Tom cannot change Noah's mind, and the boy disappears into the willows without even saying goodbye to his parents.

Joad, Pa (Tom Joad, "Old Tom")

Pa, the titular head of the family, has neither the wisdom nor the strength that his wife has, and he reluctantly defers to her judgment in one serious matter after another. Occasionally he complains of this rather bitter necessity which he considers an affront to his manhood. But he realizes his limitations and accepts the fact that, among the Joad men, Tom is more capable than he, and Al is more mechanically inclined.

Basically, Pa is a hard-working tenant farmer who does not quite understand what has happened to the old way of life. He attempts to farm in the same way as his forefathers, and every year he is forced to borrow a little more from the bank until one day the farm is no longer his. A victim of forces beyond his understanding and control, Pa is a typical migrant. He is obviously delighted when the family gets employment in California picking cotton, for this is the kind of work he understands. He does not seem to realize that, with the surplus of workers, the job will not last long.

Pa never seems to quite grasp the social overtones of their situation. At first he does not want to take Jim Casy along, fearing there will not be enough food for an extra mouth. Ma points out, in her naturally generous way, that they are already overloaded, so one more or less won't matter.

At the Hooverville, Pa does not understand why the whole camp is to be burned down just because Floyd struck a deputy. Tom has to convince the family of the danger, and again it is Tom who decides to head for the government camp where they enjoy one of the few respites in their long struggle for a decent living.

Pa's one independent effort, his attempt to build a dam around the boxcar to keep out the flooding waters, ends in failure. This is Pa's last personal attempt to cope with a hostile environment and, recognizing his inadequacy, he now looks to Ma for instructions on when they must leave the flooded area. He presents a tragic, beaten figure as he sloshes through the waist deep water with Rose of Sharon on his back. And yet, while Pa may be a failure as a leader, he is obviously a very good man.

Joad, Ruthie

Ruthie, aged twelve, is the younger Joad daughter. She is such a tomboy that, at times, she is barely distinguishable from her brother Winfield. The two children are real Katzenjammer kids, getting into one humorous scrape after another and providing a little comic relief for what would otherwise be an overly sombre novel. Ruthie makes a serious mistake when she boasts that her brother Tom is a killer, but this type of bragging is such a common trait among children that it is pardonable. Perhaps the most poignant aspect of Ruthie's experiences is the fear, voiced now and then by Ma, that she and Winfield are growing up like a couple of little barbarians. The children, like their parents, must fight for everything in their struggle for survival.

Joad, Tom ("Tommy")

If one were to measure dramatic importance in terms of heroism, a strong case could be made for considering either Jim Casy or Ma as the central figure of the novel. However, the protagonist, in terms of sheer dramatic development, is Tom Joad. For it is Tom who, through a painful process of searching for his own identity, gradually becomes a combined embodiment of his mother's sympathy and of Casy's thought. At the end of the novel we feel that Tom is ready to go forth and put his love of mankind and his socio-political philosophy into action.

Before reaching this apex of development however, Tom must endure a hard series of trials which literally transform his personality from that of a hot-tempered, cruelly tough, egocentric ex-con to something approaching the humanitarian serenity of his saint-like mother. When Tom emerges from prison, we see that he is interested mainly in his own personal comforts and needs. He does not feel the least bit guilty or uneasy about having killed a man, believing himself to be fully justified in pleading self-defence.

Having grown accustomed to the relatively comfortable prison life with its showers, clean sheets and regular meals, Tom is peevish as well as disappointed when he finds his home half destroyed and his people gone. Still proud, he refuses to sleep in a cave on his own family's land. Later, in California, after killing the deputy who slew Casy, Tom is only too happy to find a cave-like hideaway. Such ironic little twists of fate pursue him continually.

While Tom remains hardened against any representatives of the law and prone to sudden fits of violence, he is still fascinated by Casy's philosophical notions which appeal to his better nature. For, in spite of his somewhat callous exterior, Tom possesses a deep tenderness which he reserves, at first, for members of his own family. Ma is fully aware of her favorite son's potentialities for good, and she is afraid that something may have happened to him in prison to make him "mean-mad" like "Purty Boy Floyd". She is continually trying to restrain his natural violence which, she knows, can erupt any minute. When the truck is stopped by a mob near Bakersfield, Ma whispers conciliatory words to Tom and then praises him for not trying to fight the authorities. Rather than part with her son after he has killed Casy's murderer, Ma tries to hide him and keep him fed.

Tom's stay in the cave marks a very significant change in his personality, symbolized in his smashed, and hence altered face. The symbolic return-to-the-womb results in a very real psychological rebirth. Mulling over Casy's words and thinking of the example of the government camp at Weedpatch, Tom begins to grasp the value and necessity for concerted action. Up until this point he has relied almost entirely upon his own strength and native abilities in an effort to fight for a decent living, and he has met with nothing but abuse and mortification at the hands of the landowners and the deputies. Now he realizes that man cannot live alone, that man must join together with other men because there is strength in unity. He knows that he must move away from his own personal family and accept the whole world as his family. He is ready to carry on the work begun by Casy.

Joad, Winfield

Winfield Joad, aged ten, is the youngest member of the family. As was mentioned above, Winfield and Ruthie are as similar as two peas in a pod. Winfield is perhaps a little more adventurous than his sister and Ruthie enjoys nothing more than telling Ma about something naughty Winfield has done. The two children add a welcome touch of comic relief.

Rivers, Connie

Connie Rivers, Rose of Sharon's slim, pale-eyed, nineteen-year-old husband accompanies the Joad family to California but, once there, he abandons his wife and her unborn baby. Connie seems to go along for the ride. He never does much of the work, complains often, and plans rather vaguely to set out on his own and learn to be a radio repairman.

When the trek begins, Connie and Rose of Sharon seem infatuated with each other and very pleased with the prospect of having their first child. However, as the going gets more and more difficult, and Rose of Sharon begins to make demands upon Connie, he seems to be frightened away by the whole idea of parenthood. When Connie leaves, Pa tells Rose of Sharon that he was no good in the first place.

Rivers, Rose Of Sharon Joad ("Rosasharn")

Rose of Sharon is the older of the Joad daughters and Connie Rivers' wife. As her name suggests, she is searching for romance and beauty in life. Rose of Sharon is pregnant when we first meet her, and her constantly increasing physical discomfort coincides generally with the gradual worsening of the whole family's situation.

Once a gay, carefree, somewhat boisterous girl, Rose of Sharon has, with her pregnancy, become very preoccupied with herself and her future. Encouraged by her somewhat timid husband, she becomes petulant and insists that her unborn child will be adversely affected by every jolt and bump of the truck. Suspicious by nature, she sees every death, whether it be Grampa's demise or that of the family's pet dog, as an evil omen of what will happen to her child.

Ma coaxes Rose of Sharon along, threatening to slap her when she becomes too alarmed by her fantasies, and comforting her when she is very depressed. Once delivered of her stillborn child, Rose of Sharon seems more inclined to appreciate and try to alleviate the sufferings of others. She does not seem repelled by the thought of nursing the old man, but rather accepts the task as something inevitable, something which simply has to be done.

Structure

The Grapes of Wrath has an admirable symmetry. It is in thirty chapters. These thirty chapters fall into three main groups, each with its own locale. Chapters I-XI take place in Oklahoma. They describe the geographical and economic conditions which have forced the Joads and thousands of people like them, to abandon their homes and go west. Chapters XII-XVIII occur on Highway 66 and recount the terrifying trip of the Joads in their rickety Hudson.

Fear, love, and death accompany the Joads. As they cross the beautiful river in Chapter XVIII, they are in a sense baptized for their new life in California. Then Chapters XIX-XXX take place in that promised land, which is finer than its inhabitants, who oppress the migrants and thus force them to unite. In the land which does not keep its promises, there is only one oasis of peace and security. That is the government camp at Weedpatch (a real place in California, south of Bakersfield). When the Joads arrive there, they feel like human beings again. But there is no work. So they leave and go to the Hooper ranch, where the homicidal clash between those who own and those who need is fated to occur.

Other symmetry is apparent. Exactly half-way through the novel, Al stops the wheezing Hudson and points to the great, green valley spread out before the Joads like a land of milk and honey. They are ecstatic, awestruck. But the religious tone is immediately shattered. With her eyes on the fertile land below, Ma reports that Granma is dead. This is a climax in the book. Another is located in Chapter XXVI, which is the longest unit in the whole novel. In a sense this chapter is a microcosm of the entire narrative. It begins in the security of Weedpatch. But lack of income forces the Joads to uproot themselves from that temporary haven and migrate again. They drift toward violence. When Casy dies and Tom kills his murderer, there can be no more security for Tom. He must start to run. He begins to learn the truth of Casy's pronouncements on the Oversoul, the truth that each person is a part of mankind. The entire novel is the story of the education of the other Joads also — especially Ma, Pa, and Rose of Sharon — as to this truth. Toward the end, as Warren French acutely notes, "Tom has . . . lost his clannishness and replaced it with the concept that one must give help to anyone who needs it. Gradually the family comes to share this concept."[1]

Giving the novel a contrapuntal unity are the intercalary chapters. The reader soon comes to expect the narrative line to be interrupted every once in a while so that the specific plight of the Joads can be placed in national and historical perspective. This technique has been criticized by many scholars: for example, Charles Child Walcutt, who writes that "The need for the interchapters . . . reveals that the author's acceptance of a transcendental idea has not carried over into significant form: the themes of quest and struggle (by the Joads) and the exposition (in the interchapters) of the capitalistic dilemma of scarcity and 'overproduction' are not structurally united."[2] But other critics compare the intercalary chapters to the narrative sound track of documentary movies, long and wide views in the movies, and the chorus in Greek drama, and regard them as masterful foreshadowing essays in themselves.[3] Warren French takes conventionally oriented critics to task as follows: "Steinbeck's method of interrupting his main narrative with material that does not add directly to the history of the Joad family especially upsets those who think a storyteller's duty is to get on with the story or those fanatics about 'organic form' who are neurotically indisposed against shifts in style and subject."[4] These chapters strengthen the unity of the book if one agrees that its purpose is to present the Joads as typical victims of nature and capitalistic society.

An integral part of the structure of the novel is the intersecting tracks of decline and growth. Peter Lisca brilliantly demonstrates this pattern. The Joad family declines economically and in morale. They leave Oklahoma with some possessions, food, a car that runs, and health and hope. Gradually nature and society strip them of one thing after another, until at the end they have almost nothing and are practically without hope. But in a compensatory way, as they lose they gain: the Wilsons and the Wainwrights attach themselves to the diminishing Joads as surrogate family members; and as the Joad morale drops, Casy and then Tom develop a loyalty to more than family — that is, loyalty to mankind.

[1]Warren French, *John Steinbeck*, New York; Twayne, 1961, p. 106.

[2]Charles C. Walcutt, *American Literary Naturalism, A Divided Stream*, Minneapolis: University of Minnesota Press, 1956, p. 263.

[3]See Joseph Henry Jackson, "*The Finest Book John Steinbeck Has Written*," The New York Herald Tribune Books, April 16, 1939, p. 3; McElderry, "*The Grapes of Wrath: In the Light of Modern Critical Theory*," p. 311; Lisca, *Wide World of Steinbeck*, p. 156; and Fontenrose, *Steinbeck*, p. 69.

[4]French, *Steinbeck*, pp. 95-96.

Themes

The Grapes of Wrath is typical of Steinbeck because it combines his adoration of the land, his simple hatred of corruption resulting from materialism, and his abiding faith in the common people. The novel opens with a gripping picture of nature on the rampage but also of strong men and women unbroken by it. Dust is trying to smother the life out of everything in Oklahoma. The novel closes in rain-sodden California, but the rain-battered survivors there note that green grass is tinging the weary land with a promise that life will continue. Between drought and flood, the Joads move through an impressive variety of scenes and weathers. Surely Steinbeck is suggesting that in a land possessing such dynamism the people ought to be able to help each other over local crises. If the people could only cooperate, the forces of nature might not seem so hostile, might even be harnessed for the betterment of all mankind.

But instead of cooperating, the people compete more fiercely than beasts. In fact, they create monstrous institutions — banks, land companies, big ranches, and canneries (symbolized by tractors, fences with fat guards, and the like) — which further destroy and dehumanize the individual. Steinbeck is careful to make his point clear. Each person is entitled to his possessions, but only so long as they are tangible and personally workable. When he gathers unto himself more than he needs, separates himself from the physical fact of his holdings, and owns through documents and exerts his weight through subordinates, then he is wrong. When too few people own too much, those who enjoy too little sustenance will unite under repression and fight to take what they need to survive. Ma Joad has little food to feed her own family, but she shares her little with her fellow "have-not's." When she learns of a cotton-picking job, she communicates that knowledge to the Wainwrights, with the effect that the Joads actually earn less money. On the other hand, big farmers and canners with already more than they need depress wages to realize greater profits and even dump produce and slaughter livestock to keep prices up. (It must be added at once that Steinbeck's brief presentation of the complex agricultural problems of the late 1930's is simple to the point of naïvete.)

So Steinbeck places his faith in the little man and his instinctive ability to get together with others like himself for survival against the opposing forces of nature and the profit system. Steinbeck has Casy rephrase Emerson's concepts of the Oversoul and self-reliance. Casy may be partly comic when he does so, but only because of his verbal ingenuousness. He is far better when it comes to active example. He helps unite the prisoners in the California jail when they effectively protest against the sour food there; and his death during the abortive strike at the Hooper ranch results in more determination on the part of those who survive him, including Tom. The Joads demonstrate Emersonian self-reliance when they nurse their sputtering truck and the Wilsons' car along Highway 66 to California. Casy the talker admits that he cannot repair broken connecting-rods, but Tom and Al can. And the common people can also dig graves, rig tents, grind valves, repair flats, find food where almost none exists, pick peaches and cotton, nurse babies and cook breakfast simultaneously, lay pipe underground, and so on. They relish work. They want neither organized psalm-singing nor organized hand-outs. They want to earn their food by sweating for it.

Give the common man a chance, Steinbeck seems to say, and there will be enough to go around. Like Jefferson, Whitman, and Sandburg, the author of *The Grapes of Wrath* trusts the people. Jefferson deplored federalism and advocated agrarian democracy. Whitman made a religion out of his worship of man *en masse*. Sandburg delighted in the little guy's endurance and G.I. know-how. Some of his message seems anachronistic in the light of twentieth century industrialism. But we must remember that Steinbeck is at his best when he is writing of the great outdoors, far from the mad city crowd. And if they need to do so, urban readers can surely translate his message into terms which make sense to them, just as we all must do with the message of Thoreau's *Walden*.

Place in Literature

If *The Grapes of Wrath* were simply a novel of social protest, it would now be as dead as Upton Sinclair's *Jungle* and Ida Tarbell's *History of the Standard Oil Company*. If it were as inartistic as most proletarian fiction of the 1930's, once-startling examples of which one can hardly even name today, it would certainly not continue to be the steady publishing success it is. Like Stephen Crane's *Red Badge of Courage*, which is about a specific war of a century ago, it is also a parable of fear overcome and as such appeals universally to generations of readers. *The Grapes of Wrath* has an appeal which is timeless. It owed its inception to a specific crisis which no longer plagues the nation. But in the process of dramatizing that problem and suggesting ways in which it should be combatted, John Steinbeck gave us a gripping novel with enduring characterization and a message which is timeless. Ma Joad, Tom Joad, and Jim Casy — and in lesser ways the others as well — enact for us a story of the unending struggle of men of good will to make the promise of the land a living reality.

*The Reception of *The Grapes of Wrath* in Oklahoma

Most of us remember the sensational reception of *The Grapes of Wrath* (1939), Mr. Westbrook Pegler's column about the vile language of the book, Raymond Clapper's column about the vile language of the book, Raymond Clapper's column recommending the book to economic royalists, Mr. Frank J. Taylor's article in the *Forum* attacking factual inaccuracies, and the editorial in *Collier's* charging communistic propaganda. Many of us also remember that the Associated Farmers of Kern County, California, denounced the book as "obscene sensationalism" and "propaganda in its vilest form," that the Kansas City Board of Education banned the book from Kansas City libraries, and that the Library Board of East St. Louis banned it and ordered the librarian to burn the three copies which the library owned. These

*By Martin Shockley. From *American Literature*, XV (January, 1944).

items were carried in the Oklahoma press. The *Forum's* article was even reprinted in the Sunday section of the Oklahoma City *Daily Oklahoman* on October 29, 1939, with the editor's headnote of approval.

With such publicity, *The Grapes of Wrath* sold sensationally in Oklahoma bookstores. Most stores consider it their best seller, excepting only *Gone With the Wind*. One bookstore in Tulsa reported about one thousand sales. Mr. Hollis Russell of Stevenson's Bookstore in Oklahoma City told me, "People who looked as though they had never read a book in their lives came in to buy it."

Of thirty libraries answering my letter of inquiry, only four, including one state college library, do not own at least one copy of the book, and the Tulsa Public Library owns twenty-eight copies. Most libraries received the book soon after publication in the spring of 1939. Librarians generally agreed that the circulation of *The Grapes of Wrath* was second only to that of *Gone With the Wind*, although three librarians reported equal circulation for the two books, and one (Oklahoma Agricultural and Mechanical College) reported *The Grapes of Wrath* their most widely circulated volume. The librarians often added that many private copies circulated widely in their communities, and some called attention to the extraordinary demand for rental copies. A few libraries restricted circulation to "adults only." About half the libraries mentioned long waiting lists, Miss Sue Salmon of the Duncan Public Library reporting that "Even as late as the spring of 1940 we counted 75 people waiting." Mrs. Virginia Harrison of A. and M. College stated that the four copies there "were on waiting list practically the entire time up to March 19, 1941." After over two hundred students had signed the waiting list for the two copies in the University of Oklahoma library, faculty members donated several additional copies to the library.

The Grapes of Wrath was reviewed throughout Oklahoma to large and curious audiences. A high-school English teacher wrote that he had reviewed the book three times, at a ladies' culture club, at a faculty tea, and at a meeting of the Junior Chamber of Commerce, receiving comments ranging from one lady's opinion that Ma Joad was a "magnificent character," to a lawyer's remark that "Such people should be kept in their place." When Professor J. P. Blickensderfer reviewed the book in the library at the University of Oklahoma, so many people were turned away for lack of standing room that he repeated the review two weeks laters, again to a packed audience.

Much of what has passed in Oklahoma for criticism of *The Grapes of Wrath* has been little or nothing more than efforts to prove or to disprove the factual accuracy of Steinbeck's fiction. One of the minority supporters of the truth of Steinbeck's picture of the Okies has been Professor O. B. Duncan, Head of the Department of Sociology at A. and M. College. In an interview widely printed in Oklahoma newspapers, Professor Duncan discussed the economic and social problems which are involved.

The farm migrant as described in Steinbecks's *Grapes of Wrath,* Duncan said, was the logical consequence of privation, insecurity, low income, inadequate standards of living, impoverishment in matters of education and cultural opportunities and a lack of spiritual satisfaction.

"I have been asked quite often if I could not dig up some statistics capable of refuting the story of the *Grapes of Wrath*," Duncan related. "It cannot be done, for all the available data prove beyond doubt that the general impression given by Steinbeck's book is substantially reliable."[1]

Billed as "The one man, who above all others, should know best the farm conditions around Sallisaw," Mr. Houston Ward, county agent for Sequoyah County, of which Sallisaw is the country seat, spoke over radio station WKY in Oklahoma City on March 16, 1940, under the sponsorship of the State Agriculture Department. Under the headline "Houston B. Ward 'Tells All' About *The Grapes of Wrath*," the press quoted Mr. Ward on these inaccuracies:

> Locating Sallisaw in the dust bowl region; having Grandpaw Joad yearning for enough California grapes to squish all over his face when in reality Sallisaw is in one of the greatest grape growing regions in the nation; making the tractor as the cause of the farmer's dispossession when in reality there are only 40 tractors in all Sequoyah county. . . . People in Sequoyah county are so upset by these obvious errors in the book and picture, they are inclined to overlook the moral lesson the book teaches," Ward said.[2]

Numerous editorials in Oklahoma newspapers have refuted or debunked Steinbeck by proving that not all Oklahomans are Joads, and that not all Oklahoma is dust bowl. The following editorial, headed "GRAPES OF WRATH? OBSCENITY AND INACCURACY," is quoted from the Oklahoma City *Times,* May 4, 1939:

> How book reviewers love to have their preconceived notions about any given region corroborated by a morbid, filthily-worded novel! It is said that *Grapes of Wrath,* by John Steinbeck, shows symptoms of becoming a best seller, by kindness of naive, ga-ga reviewers. It pictures Oklahoma with complete and absurd untruthfulness, hence has what it takes. That American literary tradition is still in its nonage . . . is amply proved by the fact that goldfish-swallowing critics who know nothing about the region or people pictured in a novel accept at face value even the most inaccurate depiction, by way of alleged regional fiction. No, the writer of these lines has not read the book. This editorial is based upon hearsay, and that makes it even, for that is how Steinbeck knows Oklahoma.

Mr. W. M. Harrison, editor of the Oklahoma City *Times,* devoted his column, "The Tiny Times," to a review of the book on May 8, 1939. He wrote:

> Any reader who has his roots planted in the red soil will boil with indignation over the bedraggled, bestial characters that will give the ignorant east convincing confirmation of their ideas of the people of the southwest. . . . If you have children, I'd advise against leaving the book around home. It has *Tobacco Road* looking as pure as Charlotte Brontë, when it comes to obscene, vulgar, lewd, stable language.

Usually the editors consider the book a disgrace to the state, and when they do not deny its truth they seek compensation. One editor wrote:

> Oklahoma may come in for some ridicule in other states because of such movie mistakes as *Oklahoma Kid* and such literature as the current *Grapes of Wrath*. Nationally we may rank near the bottom in the number of good books purchased, and in the amount we pay our teachers. But when the biggest livestock and Four H club show comes along each year the nation finds out that somebody amounts to something in Oklahoma.[3]

On September 25, 1941, during the Oklahoma State Fair, the *Daily Oklahoman,* of Oklahoma City, carried a large cartoon showing the Oklahoma farmer proudly and scornfully reclining atop a heap of corn, wheat, and pumpkins, jeering at a small and anguished Steinbeck holding a copy of *The Grapes of Wrath*. The caption: "Now eat every gol-dun word of it."

Considerable resentment toward the state of California was felt in Oklahoma because California had stigmatized Oklahoma by calling all dust bowl migrants — even those from Arkansas and Texas — "Okies." One lengthy newspaper editorial was headed "So California Wants Nothing But Cream"[4] and another "It's Enough to Justify a Civil War."[5] On June 13, 1939, the *Daily Oklahoman* carried under a streamer headline a long article on the number of Californians on Oklahoma's relief rolls. In Tulsa, employees of the MidContinent Petroleum Company organized the Oklahoma's California Hecklers Club, the stated purpose being to "make California take back what she's been dishing out." The club's motto was "A heckle a day will keep a Californian at bay." A seven-point program was adopted, beginning, "Turn the other cheek, but have a raspberry in it," and ending, "Provide Chamber of Commerce publicity to all Californians who can read."[6] The *Stillwater Gazette,* in editorial approval wrote of the club: "*The Grapes of Wrath* have soured and this time it's the Californians who'll get indigestion."[7]

Numerous letters from subscribers have appeared in newspapers throughout Oklahoma. Some are apologetic, some bitter, some violent. A few have defended Steinbeck, sympathized with the Joads, and praised *The*

Grapes of Wrath. Some take the book as text for economic, social, or political preachments. Miss Mary E. Lemon, of Kingfisher, wrote:

> To many of us John Steinbeck's novel, *The Grapes of Wrath*, has sounded the keynote of our domestic depression, and put the situation before us in an appealing way. When the small farmers and home owners — the great masses upon which our national stability depends — were being deprived of their homes and sent roaming about the country, knocking from pillar to post; when banks were bursting with idle money, and insurance companies were taking on more holdings and money than they knew what to do with, Steinbeck attempted a sympathetic exposition of this status.[8]

Mr. P. A. Oliver, of Sallisaw, wrote no less emphatically:

> *The Grapes of Wrath* was written to arouse sympathy for the millions of poor farmers and tenants who have been brought to miserable ruin because of the development of machinery. . . . The people are caught in the inexorable contradiction of capitalism. As machinery is more and more highly developed, more and more workers are deprived of wages, of buying power. As buying power is destroyed, markets are destroyed. As the millions of workers are replaced by machinery in the industrial centers, the markets over the world collapse. The collapse of world markets destroyed the market for the cotton and vegetables produced by the poor farmers and tenants of Sequoyah county. Sequoyah county is a part of the world and hence suffered along with the rest of the capitalistic world in the collapse of capitalistic business. The day of free enterprise is done. The day of the little farmer is done. Had it not been for government spending, every farmer in the United States, every banker, every lawyer, every doctor, and all other professional workers and wage earners would long since have joined the Joads on the trail of tears. Better do some serious thinking before you ridicule the Joads.[9]

From September 22 to 25, 1940, a Congressional committee headed by Representative Tolan of California held hearings in Oklahoma's capitol investigating the problem of migratory workers. Apparently Oklahoma viewed with suspicion this intrusion, for as early as August 16, a newspaper editorial stated that:

> Anticipating an attempt to "smear" Oklahoma, Governor Phillips is marshalling witnesses and statistics to give the state's version of the migration. He has called on Dr. Henry G. Bennett and faculty members of the Oklahoma A. and M. College to assist in the presentation. Oklahoma has a right to resent any undue reflections on the state. If the hearing develops into a mud-slinging contest,

Oklahoma citizens have a few choice puddles from which to gather ammunition for an attack on the ham-and-egg crackpot ideas hatched on the western coast.[10]

On September 9 the *Daily Oklahoman* of Oklahoma City carried a story giving the names of the members of the committee which the governor had appointed to prepare his report. The paper stated that "Governor Phillips announced his intention to refute the 'Okies' story when the committee of congressmen come here to study conditions causing the migration." During the hearings, front-page stories kept Oklahomans alert to Steinbeck's guilt. On September 20 the *Daily Oklahoman* reported with apparent relief that "The fictional Joad family of *The Grapes of Wrath* could be matched by any state in the union, according to testimony." Next morning the same paper's leading editorial on "Mechanized Farms and 'Okies' " stated that mechanized farming was not responsible for conditions represented in *The Grapes of Wrath*. The editorial concluded, "It is a disagreeable fact, but one that cannot be ignored by men earnestly seeking the truth wherever found, that two of the chief factors that produce 'Okies' are AAA and WPA."

Under the heading " 'Grapes' Story Arouses Wrath of Governor," the Oklahoma City *Times* on October 2, 1939, printed the story of a correspondence between His Excellency Leon C. Phillips, Governor of Oklahoma, and an unnamed physician of Detroit, Michigan. The unnamed physician wrote, as quoted in the paper:

Is it at all conceivable that the state of Oklahoma, through its corporations and banks, is dispossessing farmers and sharecroppers . . . ? I am wondering whether you, my dear governor, have read the book in question." To which the governor warmly replied: "I have not read the thing. I do not permit myself to get excited about the works of any fiction writer. In Oklahoma we have as fine citizens as even your state could boast. . . . I would suggest you go back to reading detective magazines. . . .

The following news item is quoted from the Stillwater *Gazette* of March 23, 1940:

Thirty-six unemployed men and women picketed Oklahoma's state capitol for two hours Saturday calling on Governor Phillips to do something about conditions portrayed in John Steinbeck's novel, *The Grapes of Wrath*. One of their signs stated "Steinbeck told the truth." Eli Jaffee, president of the Oklahoma City Workers' alliance, said that "we are the Okies who didn't go to California, and we want jobs." Phillips refused to talk with the group. He said that he considered that the novel and the movie version of the book presented an exaggerated and untrue picture of Oklahoma's tenant farmer problem as well as an untruthful version of how migrants are received in California.

If His Excellency the Governor had been reticent as a critic of literature, the Honorable Lyle Boren, Congressman from Oklahoma, was no way abashed. The following speech, reprinted from the *Congressional Record,* was published in the *Daily Oklahoman,* January 24, 1940:

Mr. Speaker, my colleagues, considerable has been said in the cloakrooms, in the press and in various reviews about a book entitled *The Grapes of Wrath.* I cannot find it possible to let this dirty, lying, filthy manuscript go heralded before the public without a word of challenge or protest.

I would have my colleagues in Congress, who are concerning themselves with the fundamental economic problems of America, know that Oklahoma, like other States in the Union, has its economic problems, but that no Oklahoma economic problem has been portrayed in the low and vulgar lines of this publication. As a citizen of Oklahoma, I would have it known that I resent, for the great State of Oklahoma, the implications in that book. . . .

I stand before you today as an example in my judgment, of the average son of the tenant farmer of America. If I have in any way done more in the sense of personal accomplishment than the average son of the tenant farmer of Oklahoma, it has been a matter of circumstance, and I know of a surety that the heart and brain and character of the average tenant farmer of Oklahoma cannot be surpassed and probably not equalled by any other group.

Today, I stand before this body as a son of a tenant farmer, labeled by John Steinbeck as an "Okie." For myself, for my dad and my mother, whose hair is silvery in the service of building the State of Oklahoma, I say to you, and to every honest, square-minded reader in America, that the painting Steinbeck made in his book is a lie, a black, infernal creation of a twisted, distorted mind.

Some have blasphemed the name of Charles Dickens by making comparisons between his writing and this. I have no doubt but that Charles Dickens accurately portrayed certain economic conditions in his country and in his time, but this book portrays only John Steinbeck's unfamiliarity with facts and his complete ignorance of his subject. . . .

Take the vulgarity out of this book and it would be blank from cover to cover. It is painful to me to further charge that if you take the obscene language out, its author could not sell a copy. . . .

I would have you know that there is not a tenant farmer in Oklahoma that Oklahoma needs to apologize for. I want to declare to my nation and to the world that I am proud of my tenant-farmer heritage, and I would to Almighty God that all citizens of America could be as clean and noble and fine as the Oklahomans that Steinbeck labeled "Okies." The only apology that needs to be made is by the State of California for being the parent of such offspring as this author. . . .

Just nine days after Congressman Boren's speech had appeared in print, a long reply by Miss Katharine Maloney, of Coalgate, appeared on the Forum page of the Oklahoma City *Times*. I quote a few brief excerpts from Miss Maloney's letter:

> If Boren read *The Grapes of Wrath,* which I have cause to believe he did not, he would not label John Steinbeck a "damnable liar." John Steinbeck portrayed the characters in his book just as they actually are. . . . Why, if Boren wants to bring something up in congress, doesn't he do something to bring better living conditions to the tenant farmer? . . . This would make a better platform for a politician than the book. . . .

Not only politics, but the pulpit as well were moved by the book. One minister in Wewoka was quoted as praising it as a "truthful book of literary as well as social value, resembling in power and beauty of style the King James version of the bible."[11] His was decidedly a minority opinion. The other extreme may be represented by the Reverend W. Lee Rector, of Ardmore, who considered *The Grapes of Wrath* a "heaven-shaming and Christ-insulting book." As reported in the press, the Reverend Mr. Rector stated:

> The projection of the preacher of the book into a role of hypocrisy and sexuality discounts the holy calling of God-called preachers. . . . The sexual roles that the author makes the preacher and young women play is so vile and misrepresentative of them as a whole that all readers should revolt at the debasement the author makes of them. [it is] 100 percent false to Christianity. We protest with all our heart against the Communistic base of the story. . . . As does Communism, it shrewdly inveighs against the rich, the preacher, and Christianity. Should any of us Ardmore preachers attend the show which advertises this infamous book, his flock should put him on the spot, give him his walking papers, and ask God to forgive his poor soul.[12]

Other Oklahomans resented the filming of the story. Mr. Reo M'Vickn wrote the following letter, which was published in the Oklahoma City *Times* on January 26, 1940:

> After reading the preview of *Grapes of Wrath (Look,* January 16) I think the state of Oklahoma as a whole should take definite steps to prevent the use of the name of our state in such a production.

They are trying to disgrace Oklahoma and I for one am in favor of stopping them before they get started.

Oklahoma Chambers of Commerce had already tried to stop the filming of the picture. The following story is taken from the Oklahoma City *Times*, August 7, 1939:

> Neither Stanley Draper, secretary-manager of the Oklahoma City Chamber of Commerce, nor Dr. J. M. Ashton, research director of the State Chamber of Commerce, wants Twentieth Century Fox Corporation to make *Grapes of Wrath* in the "dust bowl." . . . Enough fault was found with the facts in Joseph (*sic*) Steinbeck's book on the "Okies." . . . So the two Chamber of Commerce men think someone should protest the inaccurate and unfair treatment the state seems to be about to receive in the filming of the picture. Draper is going to suggest the mayor of Oklahoma City protest, and Ashton will ask the governor to do likewise. . . .

On September 1, 1941, the *Daily Oklahoman* carried a four-column headline, "Lions to Attack 'Okie' Literature." The news story described the nature of the attack:

> Those who write smart and not so complimentary things about Oklahoma and Okies had better watch out, because the 3-A district governor of Oklahoma Lions clubs and his cabinet, at their first session here Sunday, discussed an all-out counter-offensive. . . . The district governor and a dozen members of his cabinet agreed in their meeting at the Skirvin hotel that something should be done to offset *Grapes of Wrath* publicity. . . .[13]

The opinions and incidents which I have presented are representative, by no means inclusive. There are, I should say, two main bodies of opinion, one that this is an honest, sympathetic, and artistically powerful presentation of economic, social, and human problems; the other, the great majority, that this is a vile, filthy book, an outsider's malicious attempt to smear the state of Oklahoma with outrageous lies. The latter opinion, I may add, is frequently accompanied by the remark: "I haven't read a word of it, but I know it's all a dirty lie."

The reception of *The Grapes of Wrath* in Oklahoma suggests many interesting problems, particularly pertinent to contemporary regional literature in America. Any honest literary interpretation of a region seems to offend the people of that region. Ellen Glasgow, though herself a Virginian, has been received in her native state with a coolness equal to the warmth with which Virginians have welcomed Thomas Nelson Page. Romanticizers of the Old South are local literary lions, while authors who treat contemporary problems are renegades who would ridicule their own people for the sake of literary notoriety.

A tremendous provincial self-consciousness expresses itself in fierce resentment of "outsiders who meddle in our affairs." One consistent theme in the writings of Oklahomans who attacked *The Grapes of Wrath* was that this book represents us unfairly; it will give us a lot of unfavorable publicity, and confirm the low opinion of us that seems to prevail outside the state. Rarely did someone say, "We should do something about those conditions; we should do something to help those people." Generally they said, "We should deny it vigorously; all Oklahomans are not Okies."

Properly speaking, *The Grapes of Wrath* is not a regional novel; but it has regional significance; it raises regional problems. Economic collapse, farm tenantry, migratory labor are not regional problems; they are national or international in scope, and can never be solved through state or regional action. But the Joads represent a regional culture which, as Steinbeck shows us, is now rapidly disintegrating as the result of extra-regional forces. It may well be that powerful extra-regional forces operating in the world today foreshadow the end of cultural regionalism as we have known it in America.

[1]Oklahoma City *Times*, Feb. 5, 1940.
[2]*Ibid*, March 16, 1940.
[3]*Ibid*., Dec. 5, 1939.
[4]*Ibid*., Nov. 28, 1938.
[5]*Ibid*., Aug. 6, 1938.
[6]*Stillwater Gazette*, April 26, 1940.
[7]*Ibid*.
[8]Oklahoma City *Times*, Dec. 22, 1939.
[9]Sallisaw *Democrat-American*, March 28, 1940.
[10]*Payne County News* (Stillwater), Aug. 16, 1940.
[11]Letter in my possession.
[12]Oklahoma City *Times*, March 30, 1940.
[13]The governor of district 3-A of the Lions clubs of Oklahoma is Dr. Joseph H. Marshburn, Professor of English in the University of Oklahoma.

*The Philosophical Joads

A popular heresy has it that a novelist should not discuss ideas — especially not abstract ideas. Even the best contemporary reviewers concern themselves with the entertainment value of a book (will it please their readers?), and with the impression of immediate reality which it creates. *The Grapes of Wrath*, for instance, was praised for its swift action and for the moving sincerity of its characters. But its mystical ideas and the moralizing interpretations intruded by the author between the narrative chapters were condemned. Presumably the book became a best seller in spite of these; its art was great enough to overcome its philosophy.

But in the course of time a book is also judged by other standards. Aristotle once argued that poetry should be more "philosophical" than

*By Frederic I. Carpenter. From *College English*, II (January, 1941).

history; and all books are eventually weighed for their content of wisdom. Novels that have become classics do more than tell a story and describe characters; they offer insight into men's motives and point to the springs of action. Together with the moving picture, they offer the criticism of life.

Although this theory of art may seem classical, all important modern novels — especially American novels — have clearly suggested an abstract idea of life. *The Scarlet Letter* symbolized "sin," *Moby Dick* offered an allegory of evil. Huck Finn described the revolt of the "natural individual" against "civilization," and *Babbitt* (like Emerson's "Self-reliance") denounced the narrow conventions of "society." Now *The Grapes of Wrath* goes beyond these to preach a positive philosophy of life and to damn that blind conservatism which fears ideas.

I shall take for granted the narrative power of the book and the vivid reality of its characters: modern critics, both professional and popular, have borne witness to these. The novel is a best seller. But it also has ideas. These appear abstractly and obviously in the interpretative interchapters. But more important is Steinbeck's creation of Jim Casy, "the preacher," to interpret and to embody the philosophy of the novel. And consummate is the skill with which Jim Casy's philosophy has been integrated with the action of the story, until it motivates and gives significance to the lives of Tom Joad, and Ma, and Rose of Sharon. It is not too much to say that Jim Casy's ideas determine and direct the Joad's actions.

Beside and beyond their function in the story, the ideas of John Steinbeck and Jim Casy possess a significance of their own. They continue, develop, integrate, and realize the thought of the great writers of American history. Here the mystical transcendentalism of Emerson reappears, and the earthy democracy of Whitman, and the pragmatic instrumentalism of William James and John Dewey. And these old philosophies grow and change in the book until they become new. They coalesce into an organic whole. And, finally, they find embodiment in character and action so that they seem no longer ideas, but facts. The enduring greatness of *The Grapes of Wrath* consists in its imaginative realization of these old ideas in new and concrete forms. Jim Casy translates American philosophy into words of one syllable, and the Joads translate it into action.

I

"Ever know a guy that said big words like that?" asks the truck driver in the first narrative chapter of *The Grapes of Wrath*. "Preacher," replies Tom Joad. "Well, it makes you mad to hear a guy use big words. Course with a preacher it's all right because nobody would fool around with a preacher anyway." But soon afterward Tom meets Jim Casy and finds him changed. "I was a preacher," said the man seriously, "but not no more." Because Casy has ceased to be an orthodox minister and no longer uses big words, Tom Joad plays around with him. And the story results.

But although he is no longer a minister, Jim Casy continues to preach. His words have become simple and his ideas unorthodox. "Just Jim Casy now. Ain't got the call no more. Got a lot of sinful ideas — but they seem kinda sensible'' (p. 27).† A century before, this same experience and essentially these same ideas had occurred to another preacher: Ralph Waldo Emerson had given up the ministry because of his unorthodoxy. But Emerson had kept on using big words. Now Casy translates them: ''Why do we got to hang it on God or Jesus? Maybe it's all men an' all women we love; maybe that's the Holy Sperit — the human sperit — the whole shebang. Maybe all men got one big soul ever'body's a part of'' (pp. 32-33). And so the Emersonian oversoul comes to earth in Oklahoma.

Unorthodox Jim Casy went into the Oklahoma wilderness to save his soul. And in the wilderness he experienced the religious feeling of identity with nature which has always been the heart of transcendental mysticism: ''There was the hills an' there was me, an' we wasn't separate no more. We was one thing. An' that one thing was holy.'' Like Emerson, Casy came to the conviction that holiness, or goodness, results from this feeling of unity: ''I got to thinkin' how we was holy when we was one thing, an' mankin' was holy when it was one thing.''

Thus far Jim Casy's transcendentalism has remained vague and apparently insignificant. But the corollary of this mystical philosophy is that any man's self-seeking destroys the unity of ''holiness' of nature: ''An' it (this one thing) on'y got unholy when one mis'able little fella got the bit in his teeth, an'run off his own way. . . . Fella like that bust the holiness'' (p. 110). Or, as Emerson phrased it, while discussing Nature: ''The world lacks unity because man is disunited with himself. . . . Love is its demand.'' So Jim Casy preaches the religion of love.

He finds that this transcendental religion alters the old standards: ''Here's me that used to give all my fight against the devil 'cause I figured the devil was the enemy. But they's somepin worse'n the devil got hold a the country'' (p. 175). Now, like Emerson, he almost welcomes ''the dear old devil.'' Now he fears not the lusts of the flesh but rather the lusts of the spirit. For the abstract lust of possession isolates a man from his fellows and destroys the unity of nature and the love of man. As Steinbeck writes: ''The quality of owning freezes you forever into 'I,' and cuts you off forever from the 'we' '' (p. 206). Or, as the Concord farmers in Emerson's poem ''Hamatreya'' had exclaimed: '' 'Tis mine, my children's and my name's,'' only to have ''their avarice cooled like lust in the chill of the grave.'' To a preacher of the oversoul, possessive egotism may become the unpardonable sin.

If a society has adopted ''the quality of owning'' (as typified by absentee ownership) as its social norm, then Protestant nonconformity may become the highest virtue, and even resistance to authority may become justified. At the beginning of his novel Steinbeck had suggested this, describing how ''the faces of the watching men lost their bemused perplexity and became hard and angry and resistant. Then the women knew that they were safe . . . Their men were whole'' (pp. 6-7). For this is the paradox of Protestantism: when men

†John Steinbeck, *The Grapes of Wrath,* New York; The Viking Press, 1939. All page references are to this edition.

resist unjust and selfish authority, they themselves become "whole" in spirit.

But this American ideal of nonconformity seems negative: how can men be sure that their Protestant rebellion does not come from the devil? To this there has always been but one answer — faith: faith in the instincts of the common man, faith in ultimate social progress, and faith in the direction in which democracy is moving. So Ma Joad counsels the discouraged Tom: "Why, Tom, we're the people that live. They ain't gonna wipe us out. Why, we're the people — we go on" (p. 383). And so Steinbeck himself affirms a final faith in progress: "When theories change and crash, when schools, philosophies . . . grow and disintegrate, man reaches, stumbles forward. . . . Having stepped forward, he may slip back, but only half a step, never the full step back" (pp. 204-205). Whether this be democratic faith, or mere transcendental optimism, it has always been the motive force of our American life and finds reaffirmation in this novel.

II

Upon the foundation of this old American idealism Steinbeck has built. But the Emersonian oversoul had seemed very vague and very ineffective — only the individual had been real, and he had been concerned more with his private soul than with other people. *The Grapes of Wrath* develops the old idea in new ways. It traces the transformation of the Protestant individual into the member of a social group — the old "I" becomes "we." And it traces the transformation of the passive individual into the active participant — the idealist becomes pragmatist. The first development continues the poetic thought of Walt Whitman; the second continues the philosophy of William James and John Dewey.

"One-self I sing, a simple separate person," Whitman had proclaimed. "Yet utter the word Democratic, the word En-Masse." Other American writers had emphasized the individual above the group. Even Whitman celebrated his "comrades and lovers" in an essentially personal relationship. But Steinbeck now emphasizes the group above the individual and from an impersonal point of view. Where formerly American and Protestant thought has been separatist, Steinbeck now faces the problem of social integration. In his novel the "mutually repellent particles" of individualism begin to cohere. "This is the beginning," he writes, "from 'I' to 'we'. " This is the beginning, that is, of reconstruction. When the old society has been split and the Protestant individuals wander aimlessly about, some new nucleus must be found, or chaos and anihilism will follow. "In the night one family camps in a ditch and another family pulls in and the tents come out. The two men squat on their hams and the women and children listen. Here is the node." Here is the new nucleus. "And from this first 'we,'" there grows a still more dangerous thing: 'I have a little food' plus 'I have none.' If from this problem the sum is 'We have a little food,' the thing is on its way, the movement has direction" (p. 206). A new social group is forming, based on the word "en masse." But here is no socialism imposed from above; here is a natural grouping of simple separate persons.

By virtue of his wholehearted participation in this new group the individual may become greater than himself. Some men, of course, will remain mere individuals, but in every group there must be leaders, or "representative men." A poet gives expression to the group idea, or a preacher organizes it. After Jim Casy's death, Tom is chosen to lead. Ma explains: "They's some folks that's just theirself, an' nothin' more. There's Al [for instance] he's jus' a young fella after a girl. You wasn't never like that, Tom" (p. 482). Because he has been an individualist, but through the influence of Casy and of his group idea has become more than himself, Tom becomes "a leader of the people." But his strength derives from his increased sense of participation in the group.

From Jim Casy, and eventually from the thought of Americans like Whitman, Tom Joad has inherited this idea. At the end of the book he sums it up, recalling how Casy "went out in the wilderness to find his own soul, and he found he didn't have no soul that was his'n. Says he foun' he jus' got a little piece of a great big soul. Says a wilderness ain't no good 'cause his little piece of a soul wasn't no good 'less it was with the rest, an' was whole" (p. 570). Unlike Emerson, who had said goodbye to the proud world, these latterday Americans must live in the midst of it. "I know now," concludes Tom, "a fella ain't no good alone."

To repeat: this group idea is American, not Russian; and stems from Walt Whitman, not Karl Marx. But it does include some elements that have usually seemed sinful to orthodox Anglo Saxons. "Of physiology from top to toe I sing," Whitman had declared, and added a good many details that his friend Emerson thought unnecessary. Now the Joads frankly discuss anatomical details and joke about them. Like most common people, they do not abscond or conceal. Sometimes they seem to go beyond the bounds of literary decency: the unbuttoned antics of Grandpa Joad touch a new low in folk-comedy. The movies (which reproduced most of the realism of the book) could not quite stomach this. But for the most part they preserved the spirit of the book, because it was whole and healthy.

In Whitman's time almost everyone deprecated this physiological realism, and in our own many readers and critics still deprecate it. Nevertheless, it is absolutely necessary — both artistically and logically. In the first place, characters like the Joads do act and talk that way — to describe them as genteel would be to distort the picture. And, in the second place, Whitman himself had suggested the necessity of it: just as the literature of democracy must describe all sorts of people, "en masse," so it must describe all of the life of the people. To exclude the common or "low" elements of individual life would be as false as to exclude the common or low elements of society. Either would destroy the wholeness of life and nature. Therefore, along with the dust-driven Joads, we must have Grandpa's dirty drawers.

But beyond this physiological realism lies the problem of sex. And this problem is not one of realism at all. Throughout this turbulent novel an almost traditional reticence concerning the details of sex is observed. The problem here is rather one of fundamental morality, for sex had always been a symbol

80

of sin. *The Scarlet Letter* reasserted the authority of an orthodox morality. Now Jim Casy questions that orthodoxy. On this first meeting with Tom he describes how, after sessions of preaching, he had often lain with a girl and then felt sinful afterward. This time the movies repeated his confession, because it is central to the motivation of the story. Disbelief in the sinfulness of sex converts Jim Casy from a preacher of the old morality to a practitioner of the new.

But in questioning the old morality Jim Casy does not deny morality. He doubts the strict justice of Hawthorne's code: "Maybe it ain't a sin. Maybe it's just the way folks is. Maybe we been whippin' the hell out of ourselves for nothin' " (p. 31). But he recognizes that love must always remain responsible and purposeful. Al Joad remains just "a boy after a girl." In place of the old, Casy preaches the new morality of Whitman, which uses sex to symbolize the love of man for his fellows. Jim Casy and Tom Joad have become more responsible and more purposeful than Pa Joad and Uncle John ever were: they love people so much that they are ready to die for them. Formerly the only unit of human love was the family, and the family remains the fundamental unit. The tragedy of *The Grapes of Wrath* consists in the breakup of the family. But the new moral of this novel is that the love of all people — if it be unselfish — may even supersede the love of family. So Casy dies for his people, and Tom is ready to, and Rose of Sharon symbolically transmutes her maternal love to a love of all people. Here is a new realization of "the word democratic, the word en-masse."

III

"An' I got to thinkin', Ma — most of the preachin' is about the poor we shall have always with us, an' if you got nothin', why, jus' fol' your hands an' to hell with it, you gonna git ice cream on gol' plates when you're dead. An' then this here Preacher says two get a better reward for their work" (p. 571).

Catholic Christianity had always preached humility and passive obedience. Protestantism preached spiritual nonconformity, but kept its disobedience passive. Transcendentalism sought to save the individual but not the group. ("Are they *my* poor?" asked Emerson). Whitman sympathized more deeply with the common people and loved them abstractly, but trusted that God and democracy would save them. The pragmatic philosophers first sought to implement American idealism by making thought itself instrumental. And now Steinbeck quotes scripture to urge popular action for the realization of the old ideals.

In the course of the book Steinbeck develops and translates the thought of the earlier pragmatists. "Thinking," wrote John Dewey, "is a kind of activity which we perform at specific need." And Steinbeck repeats: "Need is the stimulus to concept, concept to action" (p. 207). The cause of the Okies' migration is their need, and their migration itself becomes a kind of thinking — an unconscious groping for the solution to a half-formulated problem. Their need becomes the stimulus to concept.

In this novel a kind of pragmatic thinking takes place before our eyes. the idea develops from the predicament of the characters, and the resulting action becomes integral with the thought. The evils of absentee ownership produce the mass migration, and the mass migration results in the idea of group action: "A half-million people moving over the country. . . . And tractors turning the multiple furrows in the vacant land" (p. 207).

But what good is generalized thought? And how is future action to be planned? Americans in general, and pragmatists in particular, have always disagreed in answering these questions. William James argued that thought was good only in so far as it satisfied a particular need and that plans, like actions, were "plural" — and should be conceived and executed individually. But Charles Sanders Peirce, and the transcendentalists before him, had argued that the most generalized thought was best, provided it eventually resulted in effective action. The problems of mankind should be considered as a unified whole, monistically.

Now Tom Joad is a pluralist — a pragmatist after William James. Tom said, "I'm still layin' my dogs down one at a time." Casy replied: "Yeah, but when a fence comes up at ya, ya gonna climb that fence." "I climb fences when I got fences to climb," said Tom. But Jim Casy believes in looking far ahead and seeing the thing as a whole: "But they's different kinda fences. They's folks like me that climbs fences that ain't even strang up yet" (p. 237). Which is to say that Casy is a kind of transcendental pragmatist. His thought seeks to generalize the problems of the Okies and to integrate them with the larger problem of industrial America. His solution is the principle of group action guided by conceptual thought and functioning within the framework of democratic society and law.

And at the end of the story Tom Joad becomes converted to Jim Casy's pragmatism. It is not important that the particular strike should be won, or that the particular need should be satisfied; but it is important that men should think in terms of action, and that they should think and act in terms of the whole rather than the particular individual. "For every little beaten strike is proof that the step is being taken" (p. 205). The value of an idea lies not in its immediate but in its eventual success. That idea is good which works — in the long run.

But the point of the whole novel is that action is an absolute essential of human life. If need and failure produce only fear, disintegration follows. But if they produce anger, then reconstruction may follow. The grapes of wrath must be trampled to make manifest the glory of the Lord. At the beginning of the story Steinbeck described the incipient wrath of the defeated farmers. At the end he repeats the scene. "And where a number of men gathered together, the fear went from their faces, and anger took its place. And the women sighed with relief . . . the break would never come as long as fear could turn to wrath" (p. 592). Then wrath could turn to action.

IV

To sum up: the fundamental idea of *The Grapes of Wrath* is that of American transcendentalism: "Maybe all men got one big soul ever'body's a part of" (p. 33). From this idea it follows that every individual will trust those instincts which he shares with all men, even when these conflict with the teachings of orthodox religion and of existing society. But his self-reliance will not merely seek individual freedom, as did Emerson. It will rather seek social freedom or mass democracy, as did Whitman. If this mass democracy leads to the abandonment of genteel taboos and to the modification of some traditional ideas of morality, that is inevitable. But whatever happens, the American will act to realize his ideals. He will seek to make himself whole — i.e., to join himself to other men by means of purposeful actions for some goal beyond himself.

But at this point the crucial question arises — and it is "crucial" in every sense of the word. What if this self-reliance leads to death? What if the individual is killed before the social group is saved? Does the failure of the individual action invalidate the whole idea? "How'm I gonna know about you?" Ma asks. "They might kill ya an' I wouldn't know."

The answer has already been suggested by the terms in which the story has been told. If the individual has identified himself with the oversoul, so that his life has become one with the life of all men, his individual death and failure will not matter. From the old transcendental philosophy of identity to Tom Joad and the moving pictures may seem a long way, but even the movies faithfully reproduced Tom's final declaration of transcendental faith: "They might kill ya," Ma had objected.

"Tom laughed uneasily, 'Well, maybe like Casy says, a fella ain't got a soul of his own, but on'y a piece of a big one — an' then—'

'Then what, Tom?'

'Then it don' matter. Then I'll be aroun' in the dark. I'll be ever'where — wherever you look. Wherever they's a fight so hungry people can eat, I'll be there. Wherever they's a cop beating up a guy, I'll be there. If Casy knowed, why, I'll be in the way guys yell when they're mad, an' — I'll be in the way kids laugh when they're hungry an' they know supper's ready. An' when our folks eat the stuff they raise an' live in the houses they build — why, I'll be there. See?' " (p. 572).

For the first time in history, *The Grapes of Wrath* brings together and makes real three great skeins of American thought. It begins with the transcendental oversoul, Emerson's faith in the common man, and his Protestant self-reliance. To this it joins Whitman's religion of the love of all men and his mass democracy. And it combines these mystical and poetic ideas with the realistic philosophy of pragmatism and its emphasis on effective action. From this it develops a new kind of Christianity — not otherwordly and passive, but earthly and active. And Oklahoma Jim Casy and the Joads think and do all these philosophical things.

*Jeffersonian Agrarianism in
The Grapes of Wrath

. . . . A discussion of the agrarianism in *The Grapes of Wrath* does not pretend to serve as an interpretation of the entire novel. Nevertheless, it is my conviction that this doctrine is no less important than the other ideologies dramatized in the novel. As a matter of fact, agrarianism is closely associated with what was apparently one of the primary motives for writing the book, the desire to protest against the harsh inequities of the financial-industrial system that had brought chaos to America in the thirties. At times Steinbeck, with his curious combination of humanism and mysticism, seems to propose the substitution of agrarianism for industrialism as an antidote for what ailed the country.

During the disastrous thirties there were others who saw flaws in our economic system and had a similar solution. The manner, almost purposefulness, with which a financial-industrial society had encouraged moral and cultural aridity, even when successful in terms of production, prompted twelve Southerners to publish in 1930 *I'll Take My Stand,* a clarion call issued on a shepherd's pipe, summoning us back to the land and the somewhat feudal and gentlemanly traditions of the plantation days. In short, the Southern Agrarians were offering a positive program to place over against finance capitalism even before the full effects of the depression had been felt, and they continued their agitation in *The American Review,* a journal that flourished in this decade. This period saw also the growth of the back-to-the farm movement and the proliferation of books guaranteeing independence, and even security, on five acres.

I am not suggesting that Steinbeck was influenced by the Southerners or anyone else, but only that in this period of crumbling faiths many men turned to agrarianism as others turned to the Townsend Plan or Huey Long. Naturally, the men in the agrarian group had much in common, and certainly all of them drew upon Jeffersonian agrarianism. Because he had faith in the common man and thus gave his thinking a broad popular basis, Steinbeck was closer to Jeffersonianism than were the Southern Agrarians, who sought to resurrect not only an agricultural way of life but also the traditional cultural values of Europe. Steinbeck was concerned with democracy, and looked upon agrarianism as a way of life that would enable us to realize the full potentialities of the creed. Jefferson, of course, held the same belief.

In order to clarify the full impact of Jeffersonian thought on Steinbeck, it is necessary at least to adumbrate the nature of eighteenth century agrarianism in America. This was a doctrine informed by the spirit and principles of Jefferson. Basic to it is the belief that landed property held in freehold must be available to everyone. Jefferson took seriously his middle class heritage from Locke, placing great faith in property and the property holder. To him, equalitarian democracy meant a country made up of small farmers, and in

*By Chester E. Eisinger. From *The University of Kansas City Review,* XIV (Winter, 1947).

fighting for the abolition of entail and primogeniture in Virginia he tried to achieve a commonwealth dominated by precisely this group. Although Jefferson himself never went so far, many Jeffersonians agreed that if a man could not get legal title to landed property, he could claim ownership to land he occupied and tilled by virtue of a natural right. Possession of his own land gave the small farmer control of the means of production. It followed therefore that such a man could be economically independent, for he would be obligated to no man, he could reap what he sowed, and his agricultural way of life would make for a relatively high degree of self-sufficiency. It also followed that such a man would be politically independent, inasmuch as no one held a coercive power over him; no part of his way of life or his security was threatened by an outside force. The independent freehold farmer was a complete individualist, so the Jeffersonian myth goes, who acted in accordance with his own instincts or desires and rose or fell by virtue of his own efforts. Mostly he rose because he was a moral man; God had made his breast "His peculiar deposit for substantial and genuine virtue." History does not record the corruption of an agricultural people. In other words, agrarianism has a sprinkling of primitivism. Close contact with nature and with God makes and keeps men pure. By contrast the city is a cesspool of evil. Immorality thrives there, alongside of business and finance. These latter rob the common man of economic and political independence and destroy the dominant position of the farmer in the affairs of the state. Jeffersonian agrarianism, then, was essentially democratic: it insisted on the widespread ownership of property, on political and economic independence, on individualism; it created a society in which every individual had status; it made the dignity of man something more than a political slogan.

I

Seven books preceded *The Grapes of Wrath*, but in only one of them do we have any foretaste of Steinbeck's predilection for agrarianism. True, in *The Pastures of Heaven, To a God Unknown,* and *The Long Valley* he had dealt with tillers of the soil and with ranchers, but in these books he was preoccupied with psychological analysis, and the tone was mystical and nostalgic. Although dealing with agricultural workers, *In Dubious Battle* is concerned essentially with a strike and a scientist. But *Of Mice and Men* shows clearly Steinbeck's interest in agrarianism, even though he is still haunted by psychological abnormality.

In this latter book we have the disenchanted and disinherited if not the dispossessed of *The Grapes of Wrath*. Lennie and George, migratory workers in the California fields, cherish the dream of a little farm of their own where, as Lennie's refrain has it, they can *"live off the fatta the lan'."* George yearns for his own place where he could bring in his own crops, where he could get what comes up out of the ground. He wants the full reward of his own labor. He wants the independence that ownership can give him. Nobody could fire him if the farm were his. If someone came he didn't like, he could say, " 'Get the hell out,' and by God he's got to do it." They would produce all they could eat, and then: "We'd jus' live there. We'd belong there. . . . We'd have our own place where we belonged and not sleep in no bunk house." A stake in society and status in society — these give men the dignity that is rightfully theirs in a democracy. Productive property, Steinbeck seems to suggest, is a real restorative. Even Candy, the used up sweeper, and Crooks, the misshapen Negro, are reinvigorated by the prospect of ownership and stability.

Of Mice and Men, however, was a sentimental and slight book. Three years later, in *The Grapes of Wrath*, Steinbeck was able to present a fuller exposition of his agrarian views. Early in the novel he introduces the conflict between the farmer and the financial-industrial interests of the city. The truck driver remarks to Tom that the tractors are pushing the croppers off the land. The full significance of this observation is not apparent until we come to the fifth chapter. Here Steinbeck makes clear that the tractors are the instruments of a mysterious financial system, just as some men represent that system. These men are deprived of will and personality by the system and its machine. When they must tell the croppers to get off the land, they shed their humanity and take refuge in the cold mathematics of the system. From now on there will be a tractor and a superintendent on the land, not the people. And the land will be raped methodically, without passion. It will be productive because it yields a crop, but it will be sterile too because no one loves or hates it and because it will bear under iron and die under iron. The sterility of machine culture is emphasized by Steinbeck's comment, much later in the book, on the languid, heat-raddled ladies, parasites on that culture, whose sexual intercourse is safe, odorless, and unproductive. The animosity to the city is emphasized in the bitter attitude toward business ethics, summed up best perhaps in the incident of the tire with the broken casing. "You go steal that tire an' you're a thief, but he tried to steal your four dollars for a busted tire. They call that sound business." Finally, Steinbeck remarks how the business men farmers, those who keep books but never follow the plow, buy up the canneries in California, cut off the small farmer's market, and eventually take the property away from him. Chiefly in negative terms Steinbeck is showing us that the farmer is the productive, healthy member of society. He suggests a primitivistic conception of nature: that the farmer draws spiritual strength as well as sustenance from the soil. Antithetical to these notions is the aridity of the city-bred rich woman, the dishonesty of business, and the essentially inhuman and unproductive nature of the machine age.

Precisely what was it that this sick business culture was destroying? Very briefly it was a way of life that was based on the retention of the land. The Okies had their roots deep in the land, and they didn't want to be shoved off it. Grampa took up the land, and Pa was born here, and we were born here. It's our land. "We measured it and broke it up. We were born on it, and we got killed on it, died on it. Even if it's no good, it's still ours. That's what makes it ours — being born on it, working it, dying on it. That makes ownership, not a paper with numbers on it." The Okies argue, in other words, that occupying the land and devoting one's labor to it are the criteria of ownership, and that these transcend the legal right to the land represented by the title. These two criteria are the backbone of the natural right argument current in the eighteenth century: men had a natural right to as much land as they could profitably use. This natural right assumption gave sanction to the squatter whose heritage passed down into the nineteenth century, and even into the twentieth. For when the Okies want to work a little patch of ground lying fallow, the California police chase them off. "You goddamned squatters. Pretty soon you'd think you owned it. You'd be sore as hell. Think you owned it. Get off now . . . the cop was right. A crop raised — why, that makes ownership."

When you are shoved off the land and can exercise neither a legal nor a natural right to possess land, then you have lost status and your life has lost meaning. There is a kind of mystic exaltation in the ownership of property which the farmer experiences. Crévecoeur called it "the bright idea of property." Steinbeck's anonymous tenant knows it too. " 'If a man owns a little property, that property is him, it's part of him, and it's like him. If he owns property only so he can walk on it and handle it and be sad when it isn't doing well, and feel fine when the rain falls on it, that property is him, and some way he's bigger because he owns it'." So, then, is he smaller when he loses it. When the tractor knocked over the elder Tom's house and drove him from the land, it took something out of him; he was never the same. Grampa can't survive the loss of the homestead. At the last moment he refuses to leave. " 'This country ain't no good, but it's my country.' " When he dies en route to California, Casy says shrewdly. " 'An' Grampa didn' die tonight. He died the minute you to 'im off the place'." If Grampa could not survive being torn up by the roots, at least he escaped the indignities that the others must endure because they are landless. They are called bums by the proprietor of a camping ground; Pa mildly protests. " 'It's dirt hard for folks to tear up an' go. Folks like us that had our place. We ain't shif'less. Till we got tractored off, we was people with a farm'." We were cropping, but we used to own the land. Pa must remind himself and the others that nobody calls a freehold farmer a shiftless bum. He is a broken man who must find solace in the past. Ma, too, recalls the dignity of the Joad heritage. " 'We don't look up to nobody. Grampa's grampa, he fit in the Revolution. We was farm people till the debt. And then — them people. They done somepin to us . . . made me feel mean. Made me feel ashamed'." They — the California police, the owners of the orchards — had worked on the spirit of the Okies and worn it down. The pride of the freeholder withers after dispossession, and his function in life disappears.

The way of life normal to the farmer is the productive life. Fallow land, when men are starving, is a sin. The uniform impulse among the Okies is to get hold of an acre and make something grow on it. In this way they hope to gain some slight measure of security. Unfortunately, the California land has all been "stolen" by the early American settlers who took it from the Mexicans. "They put up houses and barns, they turned the earth and planted crops. And these things were possession, and possession was ownership." Those who were now the great owners had exercised a natural right to get the

87

land, and now they held it, aware that "when property accumulates in too few hands it is taken away." In a dynamic American society, the feverish Americans who had utilized a radical doctrine to gain the land had now become the conservative, stable element while a new radical group arose, the dispossessed Okies. Now these latter wanted the land. The Okies are Steinbeck's protagonists in a kind of revolutionary social action which is as American as Jefferson's successful efforts to abolish entail and primogeniture; and this action would yield the same results — a wider distribution of property. Thus it is that when Tom takes his last leave of Ma, going forth to carry on the work of Casy, who has died a martyr to the cause of social justice, he reflects on the Okie-run government camp where there was better order than the police had ever been able to establish in areas of their jurisdiction. " 'I been awonderin' why we can't do that all over. Throw out the cops that ain't our people. All work together for our own thing — all farm our own lan'." But what are you going to do? demands the practical Ma. " 'I been thinkin' a hell of a lot, thinkin' about our people livin' like pigs, an' the good rich lan' layin' fallow, or maybe one fella with a million acres, while a hundred thousan' good farmers is starvin'. An' I been wonderin' if all our folks got together an' yelled, like them fellas yelled, only a few of 'em at the Hooper ranch . . .' " The democratic way for Steinbeck is to achieve through collective action the individual security on the land that Jefferson prized so highly. When men farm their own land they will run their own society.

II

It is clear, I think, that Steinbeck has much in common with Jeffersonian agrarianism and that he is attracted to the doctrine because he has the same humanistic interest in democracy that Jefferson had. It remains to inquire if agrarianism, its form and substance, is the part of the Jeffersonian tradition that we should preserve. Certainly we could use today many of the virtues attributed to the independent yeoman by Jefferson. But I fear that we cannot use and cannot achieve agrarianism as a formal way of life. Its champions of the thirties have apparently realized the futility of running counter to the temper of the times. *The American Review* is dead, and pretty well buried in the libraries. Many of the Southern Agrarians have turned their backs on social problems and have become engrossed in an authoritarian kind of aesthetics.

Steinbeck himself, if we are to judge by *Cannery Row* and *The Wayward Bus*, has abandoned any serious consideration of the problems of political economy.

The bankruptcy of Jefferson's ideal is only too well illustrated in the fact that the family size farm continues to disappear from the American scene. It would seem that the survival of an idea, or even its resurrection in troubled times, is no proof of its validity. In the great war just passed we have seen the triumph of American capitalism (Louis Hacker's phrase) and of American industrial strength. The machine age, or the atomic age, is fastened upon us and growing apace. Almost alone now, Luis Bromfield is repeating the axioms of the Physiocrats and calling us back to the land. Nobody listens.

We must seek another road to the independence and security and dignity that we expect from democracy.

*The Grapes of Wrath
In the Light of Modern Critical Theory

The social problem which made the Joads of national significance in 1939 has disappeared or changed its form. The artistic problem of their chronicle remains. Now, as in 1939, the devil asks the conundrum of the workshop: "It's clever, but is it *art*?" To literary students the question is important, for it seems likely that in the generation to come we shall have more rather than less of propaganda literature. . . .

The attempt is the more timely, because of the present emphasis on critical values and methods. In discussing *The Grapes of Wrath*, I am going to use a number of ideas found in two recent books of critical theory published by the Princeton University Press; they are *The Intent of the Critic* and *The Intent of the Artist*. (The distinction of the titles is unimportant, for even an artist turns critic when he talks about his art.) Each of these books is in form a symposium, with no great unity of plan. Though not intended to be a consistent body of doctrine, these books do bring together conveniently a number of ideas actually operative in the making and reading of contemporary literature. If, then, we take these ideas, we have a tangible basis for evaluating the novel; and, conversely, we have our experience with the novel as a check on the theories.

First, let us consider the old question of the basic relationship of art and reality, a point most fully discussed by Mr. Centeno in his Introduction to *The Intent of the Artist*. He asserts that there are two theories of art: art is an irreducible activity, a love activity complete within itself and justified by its own existance; or art is merely a pleasanter way of representing materials found in purer form elsewhere. Of these two theories, Mr. Centeno prefers the first; in fact, he denies the validity of the second. According to which theory, then, was *The Grapes of Wrath* written? Or does either theory sufficiently account for the novel?

It is certainly true that Steinbeck does seem in a sense to be in love with his characters and with the living tissue of their experience. One thinks of Tom Joad going home from prison, of his welcome when he finds his family the next morning, of Grampa's funeral at the roadside. Such scenes do illustrate Mr. Centeno's observation that an artist is "a man who cannot separate himself from livingness". Parenthetically, I may remark that I do not consider "livingness" a term of great beauty; but as a paraphrase for "vividness" it at least avoids the hackneyed, smooth-worn quality of that overused term.

*By B. R. McElderry, Jr. From *College English,* V (March, 1944).

Yet in spite of the "livingness," or the love of life, embodied in Steinbeck's depiction of scene and character, it is true that parts of the novel — the rage against the bankers of Oklahoma, the camp life of the Okies in California, the fruit-ranch strike — may fairly be described as a "pleasanter" representation of facts to be found in purer form elsewhere. Carey McWilliams' *Factories in the Fields,* a contemporary work of popular economics and sociology, affords convenient comparison. In factual truth McWilliams' work is fuller and more authentic; though at the same time Steinbeck's novel is more lively, or, to use Mr. Centeno's angular term, more full of "livingness." The novel might thus be said to illustrate both the theories of art described by Mr. Centeno. Yet Mr. Centeno has presented these two theories as mutually exclusive; in so far as the novel competes with *Factories in the Fields,* he would say, it is false and unsatisfactory as a work of art.

Further on in his discussion, however, we find Mr. Centeno asserting that "the work of art is not meant to be a corroboration of our sense of experience, but an expansion of it." Now, obviously, the sense of experience must be corroborated before it can be expanded. In *The Grapes of Wrath*, for instance, the foreclosures of Oklahoma, the camp life of California, and the fruit-ranch strike must be made plausible before their effect on the characters becomes of interest. Thus Mr. Centeno's original statement of the two theories as opposed and mutually exclusive seems misleading. It illustrates, I believe, the favorite academic sin of thinking in categories instead of in dynamics. If *The Grapes of Wrath* is a bad novel, it cannot reasonably be condemned on the grounds that it is sociological. It would be impossible to write a novel on the Okies that would not be sociological. It is possible, however, that the sociology might be inartistically presented or that the sociology might be bad to begin with.

Before proceeding further with this basic issue, let us consider the related point of unity — an old requirement for a work of art. To the familiar idea of the vital relationship between author, subject, and reader, Mr. Centeno introduces a new subtlety of terminology. Thus the intent of the artist is distinguished from his intentions. His intentions are conscious, willed purposes; while the intent, subconscious and innate, is represented as more deeply vital, and hence especially characteristic of the masterpiece.

In terms of *The Grapes of Wrath*, I take this distinction to mean something like this. Steinbeck's intention was to write a story of the Joad family in its struggle to adapt itself to new, unfavorable conditions. In carrying out this conscious intention and in writing the various scenes which represent subintentions, Steinbeck's real interest — his subconscious motivation — is to express his basic faith in mankind, in the courage, the endurance, and the kindliness of people like the Joads, and to show their passionate yearning for opportunity and for justice. It is the presence of this intent which gives power to the intention — that is, if one concedes that the novel is successful.

The content of the work of art, says Mr. Centeno, must be formally organized in accordance with the creative intent. Thus, in *The Grapes of Wrath* the first quarter of the volume concerns preparations for the trip west;

the second quarter, the trip itself, and the latter half, the sequence leading to Tom's escape, Al's engagement, and the birth of Rosasharn's baby. This cycle of events, I believe, is adequate to embody the intent: Steinbeck's feeling for the fundamental nature of his characters.

The relation of the work of art to the reader or audience is termed by Mr. Centeno its "extent." In securing extent — or perhaps one might substitute the common phrase "reader-interest" — the intent must not be sacrificed or impaired. In *The Grapes of Wrath*, for example, it might be a question as to whether the freedom of language is always essential to the intent, or whether a few "sons-of-bitches" are sometimes thrown in to increase the extent of the book among certain readers. More seriously, some passages might be considered as direct propaganda and hence a distraction from the basic intent. My own conclusion based on a fourth reading of the novel, is that it does have "integral creative oneness," in Mr. Centeno's exact but cumbersome phrase. The intent seems to me clear and steady; the content well selected, arranged, and proportioned; and the extent, or communication of intent to the reader, is adequate. One notable exception is the concluding detail in which Rosasharn gives her breast to the starving stranger. This incident, clearly symbolic of the basic intent, is, nevertheless not sufficiently plausible to communicate it. Coming at the very end of the novel the incident is an important exception. This, and perhaps a few other details aside, however, the novel remains "interesting," not "exteresting," in Mr. Centeno's use of these terms. In the historical sense any novel about the Okies would be exteresting if it contained something of factual or sociological truth. But a novel on this subject would be interesting only if it were felt integrally — that is, if it had inner unity. Such an inner unity I believe *The Grapes of Wrath* has.

Turning to *The Intent of the Critic*, we find in Mr. Ransom's discussion of poetry two ideas which may, I think, be adapted to the discussion of the novel. First, says Mr. Ransom, "a poem is more than its paraphrase." Now, in the loose sense of the term, anything printed or spoken is more than its paraphrase, but the implication of Mr. Ransom's statement is that a poem must, in the actual line-for-line reading of it, create itself. The means by which it does this, he says, are its structure and texture; these, then, are the proper — or most important — considerations for the critic.

That structure is as valuable to a novel as it is to a poem is well illustrated by *The Grapes of Wrath*. Yet it has not been sufficiently recognized, I think, that *The Grapes of Wrath* — like the *Odyssey, Pilgrim's Progress,* and *Robinson Crusoe* — is formulated as a journey. This structural device — one of the simplest, oldest, and most vital in literature — is well suited to the theme or intent of the story: the search for opportunity and justice. This, I believe, will be generally admitted. The ending of the story, however (not the Rosasharn incident previously mentioned, but the final disposition of the characters), has been severely criticized. I remember a friend of mine saying: "It doesn't have any ending." This, he felt, was a defect in the novel which clearly revealed the author's incompetence. But the lack of an ending in any final sense is in keeping with the basic idea of the novel. The continued faith in the search, in spite of failure to find opportunity and justice, is far more effective than a trumped-up ending (such as the conclusion to *Robinson Crusoe*) would be. In a way, the uncompleted journey toward opportunity and justice is parallel to the modern tragedy, which decrees life, not death, for its hero.

Of the texture of a novel it is difficult to speak without long extracts. Several points, however, may be indicated briefly. There is the dialogue, with its rich, illiterate idiom; the description — set pieces, like the turtle crossing the road, and details which help us realize such a scene as the government camp; narrative episodes, such as the desert ride; and dramatic scenes, such as the burning of Hooverville. One may say that the texture is varied; that the pace is swift; that the story is fully rather than barely told. And one may say that the temptation to skip — even in re-reading — seldom appears.

A special problem is presented by the notable interludes, which treat the background of the Joads' experience: the opening chapter, descriptive of the dust bowl; the sale of household goods and the purchase of secondhand cars, set forth in a strangely generalized but vivid dialogue; the decay of the vacant houses; and the chaos of U.S. Highway 66. Of the thirty chapters in the novel, fourteen are interludes of this sort, though they occupy less than a hundred of its six hundred pages. They are Steinbeck's chief departure from conventional technique, and obviously they are a departure only in degree. Novelists have always felt free to elaborate the physical and social setting of the story. Steinbeck's interludes enrich the texture of his novel, and they do it far more subtly than, say, the moral essays of Fielding; or the "Dear Reader" passages of Dickens and Thackeray; or, to come closer to date, the elaborate author-interpretation of Galsworthy. To change the basis of comparison, the interludes have much the same justification and effectiveness as the familiar "long shots" of the movies. Of the fourteen interludes, only five are bare and direct social criticism voiced by the author rather than his characters. These are the conception of the soulless banks and corporations in Chapter V; the concept of Manself as opposed to ownership in Chapter XIV; the history of landowner-ship in California; the Californian suspicion of the Okies; and the indictment of waste under the profit system. In defense of these passages it may be said that they comprise barely twenty-five pages of the six-hundred-page novel; that they are so spaced as to bear upon the story itself (for example, the history of landownership in California comes just before the Joads enter Hooverville); that their literature eloquence points up the colloquial tone of the book as a whole. Leave these passages out, and something valuable, something pertinent, is gone.

Approval of the novel on the basis of its structure and texture, however, would not satisfy Mr. Norman Foerster, whose essay sets up ethical consid-erations as equally important with aesthetic ones. It is, he says, the business of the artist to achieve aesthetic and ethical values together, in whatever way he can; it is the business of the critic to distinguish between these values. From the poetry he gives two brief examples of such discrimination. Of Wordsworth's "Tintern Abbey" he says that it "is great aesthetically; as we have come increasingly to see, it is ethically vital, but unsound; in sum, this poem is a superb expression of unwisdom.'' And of Longfellow's ''Psalm of Life'' Mr. Foerster remarks that it is ''bungling in its art, stereotyped in its wisdom.''

Leaving these two judgments to private debate, let us apply the principle to *The Grapes of Wrath*. Is this novel ethically sound? Is it a wise book? And, to revert to an earlier point, is it good sociology? One may guess from his other writings that Mr. Foerster would say ''No'' to all these questions. For it is undeniable that *The Grapes of Wrath* does embody a strong faith in the natural goodness of man — a doctrine abhorrent to Mr. Foerster. In Steinbeck's eyes the Joads are all good people. They may be weakly good, like Pa or Rosasharn; or they may be strongly good, like Ma Joad and Tom. But their ill fortune is never represented as due to their own tragic flaws. Conversely, all persons in power or authority — with the exception of the director of the government camp — are represented as evil. Greed creates fear, and fear creates injustice. As Steinbeck himself puts it: ''The quality of owning freezes you forever into 'I,' and cuts you off forever from the 'We.' ''

One may admit much truth in this simple formula of good and evil and still feel that it is inadequate. The clear implication in the novel that the formula is complete, is disquieting. It arouses a suspicion that the characters — vivid as they are — are only half-truths, too. This is the more plausible, since all the real characters are drawn from one level of society. We follow the action steadily from the point of view of the Okies. People of other social strata are presented as enemies, portrayed in a single aspect, never seen from the inside.

Is this, perhaps, the clue to Edmund Wilson's comment (in *The Intent of the Critic*) that Steinbeck's novels represent almost the exact line between good and bad art? *The Grapes of Wrath* is a shrewd novel, a lively pattern of experience, varied and skilful in texture; but it may be attacked as basically sentimental. Ma Joad's remark, so effectively used to provide an ending for the Hollywood version of the story, expresses the fundamental weakness: ''Rich fellas come up an' they die, and their kids ain't no good, an' they die out. But, Tom, we keep a-comin'. Don't you fret, Tom. A different time's comin'.'' The poor struggle for riches, success, power; but those who achieve them die out. Life is, then, a sort of squirrel cage or treadmill. Such a view gives no basis for faith in a brighter future. The assertion that the brighter future is coming — stated by Ma Joad and implied by Steinbeck — is thus mere sentimental optimism. This is a fault, by the way, ascribed to Steinbeck's more recent novel, *The Moon Is Down*.

Yet, as someone remarked, the epithet ''sentimental'' may easily be used as a club to beat people we don't like. I have no desire to use it as such, for the truth is that most English and American novelists are sentimental. We are a sentimental people, and when we rebel against conventional sentiment we get sentiment in reverse à la James T. Farrell or à la Ernest Hemingway. Or, to take more comparable material, consider for a moment Erskine Caldwell's *Tobacco Road*. Is the spectacle of total depravity offered in this production more intelligent and therefore less sentimental than the natural goodness of the downtrodden implied in *The Grapes of Wrath?* In short, while I believe that sentimentality is a valid charge against *The Grapes of Wrath*, I do not believe it is a very important one; for the sentimentality, so far as it exists, rests on an incomplete view of life, not upon frustration.

The importance of a positive quality in literature is interestingly touched upon by W. H. Auden in what I regard as the most notable essay in these two Princeton volumes. Mr. Auden bravely essays the difficult mission of prophecy, and in doing so he puts life first and art second. Emphasizing the interdependence of ethics, science, politics, and aesthetics, he asserts that "the attempt to make aesthetics an autonomous province has resulted in academic aesthetics, and the substitution of the pedant for the priest." In place of such exclusive specialization, the democratic society requires increasing skill in communication; for the essence of democracy, he says, is to work toward an increasingly "open" society. By an "open" society he means one in which talent and ideas have free flow.

Though Mr. Auden in this essay is prescribing for the critic, this conception of the "open" society has considerable bearing on the proper nature of art. It may be said, for instance, that *The Grapes of Wrath* is a novel vigorously sympathetic to the "open" society. The novel skilfully communicates attitudes of a relatively inarticulate group or type. It enthusiastically bridges the gap between art, politics, and ethics, making most unhappy the pedantic student of aesthetics, intent on playing the old static game of categories. In short, *The Grapes of Wrath* was not merely a timely book on intinerant farm laborers; it was — and is — creative in the best sense. Sentimentality may impair, but does not cancel, its value. The sociological content of the novel, far from making it an "impure" work of art, as Mr. Centeno might wish us to believe, has, in fact, made it a more vital work of art.

In making these tentative applications of critical theory, I have carefully refrained from prophesying immortality for Steinbeck's novel. It may be, indeed, that we have arrived at an epoch in which literary immortality will be unattainable. So many books are published; so few, even of the best, are re-read; and there are so many reading publics almost independent of one another that the dominance required to establish a classic is steadily more difficult to achieve. But, if classics are to emerge from the first forty years of this century, I can think of not more than a dozen novels in America that are so likely or such fit candidates for that measure of immortality.

Review Questions and Answers

Question 1.

Discuss the idea of a Transcendental "Oversoul" as it appears in the novel.

Answer

It is Jim Casy who first brings up, in folk idiom, the concept that, translated, resembles the Oversoul propounded by the American Transcendentalists, especially Ralph Waldo Emerson. The Transcendentalists defined "Oversoul" as a sense of oneness with God, with nature and with other individuals. The discovery of the Oversoul had to be made through intuition; that is, a person felt or sensed this truth, rather than saw it as a tangible fact. Jim Casy, the ex-preacher, has been doing a lot of thinking because he has found the religion of Bible-belt evangelism no longer adequate to his needs or the needs of his people. He has come up with the idea that the "spirit of God" — for in his country any version of religion has always included the idea of "spirit" and "getting the spirit" — may be instead the human spirit. And instead of separate souls, every single person's soul — and apparently the word *spirit* can be used synonymously — may go to make up part of "one big soul." At several points in the novel he renews the discussion of one big inclusive soul that holds together, unites all people. It can be seen that such an idea also fits in with the concept of the family unit and the social philosophy of group action developed in the book.

Question 2.

What would you say is the social philosophy developed in *The Grapes of Wrath?*

Answer

Theoretically, it could be considered as based upon the ideas of Marx and Lenin and other socialist thinkers of the past and present. Yet the social philosophy which develops in this novel is peculiarly American, founded on what might be termed loosely "the American Dream": the principle of democracy, of course, including the rights due to all under such a system; the pioneer spirit of endurance which first explored and settled the Middle West and the West; the will to forge ahead and succeed — drive (even though the undesirable effects of this same urge are revealed in the form of grasping materialism and ruthless power interests in the novel). Specifically, the social theory which develops and is realized in action in *The Grapes of Wrath* — through the efforts of the Jim Casys, the Tom Joads and those who choose to follow them — is that which urges that the small people, the poor people, those most in a position to be exploited and denied by the power of the profit hungry, must amass strength through banding together and taking group action. As the novel progresses, this idea first takes the form of worried, angry conversations among the frustrated men: "We have guns. What if we banded together to fight the owners, the banks, the deputy sheriffs?" There are some past examples before them — i.e., the mountain men who revolted successfully in Akron, Ohio against rubber companies. There is the present working example of the essentially socialist community of the government camp at Weedpatch: there the people manage all their own affairs — government, economy, policing, health, recreation (along the lines of the modern

Israeli *kibbutz*) — and they also keep out unwarranted intrusion and intimidation from outsiders to the camp. "Advanced" social theory (for the period under consideration — the depression and post-depression years) is also realized, at length, in that the jobless and starving men come to understand the nature of "unions" and "strikes," along with the violence of "strikebreaking," unfortunately. At the end of the novel Tom Joad, who has killed a deputy sheriff in defence of Jim Casy, brutally murdered for his "agitation" for a union and for strikes to get fair wages, has set forth to work toward this same social ideal. For the one ruthless social lesson learned by the Joads and their like in the novel is that "separately we are weak, together we have strength."

Question 3.

Briefly describe the biographical and historical background which produced *The Grapes of Wrath*. Given this context, how was the novel received at its publication, and more recently?

Answer

First of all, John Steinbeck knew intimately the country and the people about which he wrote. Born and raised in the Salinas Valley in California, he lived most of his first forty years there (and much of his writing was set in that locale). Furthermore, in the mid-thirties he became aware of and disturbed about the conditions of migrant workers in general (he had observed them in his own countryside, in California) and the plight of those who were forced to flee from the Dust Bowl of parts of Kansas and Oklahoma in particular. He wrote newspaper articles on the subject in 1935 and 1937, having gone to Oklahoma and made the westward trek to California with the migrant workers themselves. (The latter series of articles was published as a pamphlet called *Their Blood Is Strong*.) It needs hardly be added that other published commentary of the period — excepting that which defended certain ownership and public interests in the states most involved, such as California and Oklahoma — corroborates Steinbeck's journalistic findings which he metamorphosed into fiction.

At its publication in 1939 the novel was received essentially as a social document and a work of social protest, by both its admirers and its detractors. It was acclaimed, even in the form of a Pulitzer Prize to Steinbeck; it was widely discussed and debated in newspapers, magazines and on the radio; it was of course turned into a movie; and it was in some places banned and burned, for its so-called revolutionary socio-economic theories (for the charge of "Red" was as panicked, as all-inclusive and as vaguely defined at that period of American history as it has been in more recent years), for its so-called unfair and untrue report of the conditions of migrant laborers, and for its so-called dirty language.

When some of the first furor over the novel died down, however, critics began to look at it from an artistic point of view and to ask the question which is still being asked and answered pro and con — is it art or propaganda? Or, in fact, does one have to choose between the two? Critics of each decade since its publication have tended to look upon it with the going critical attitudes and habits of their group, with a general shift from the sociological readings toward artistic critiques which include everything from Steinbeck's various philosophies (humanism, pragmatism, biological theory of man, non-teleological thought, agrarianism — how well these come across in the context of the novel), his alternations between the dreamlike and the real (fantasy, allegory, symbolism), his ideas of good and evil, the individuality or universality of his characters, his mystical symbolism.

Question 4.
How can the word *humanism* be applied to *The Grapes of Wrath*?

Answer
All the major characters in the novel, with Jim Casy and later, Tom Joad leading, seem to move from a religiously based to a humanly based philosophy of life in the novel. It is clear, of course, as soon as Jim Casy begins to explain to everyone why he cannot be a "preacher" any longer that he more and more finds the religious precepts of his and his people's immediate past untenable in their present realities: some of Jim's most memorable speeches early in the book are his declarations that he wants to help and comfort the people still, he feels things are changing and they are going someplace, but he can no longer look upon sin in the conventional Bible-belt evangelical way nor can he offer facile prayers or parade future heavenly glory to people whose lives are materially and psychically wretched in the present. In another important speech he claims the "sperit" — a feeling of which has always figured so largely in local religion — seems now to him to be more of a *human* spirit than the spirit of a remote God; at any rate it is this human spirit which he now feels sure of, just as he feels certain that the souls of all the people go to make up one great soul: the Oversoul spoken of before.

Tom Joad moves toward a philosophy of humanism in the novel, too. At the beginning, although he is a sensitive, kind and communicative person, he is still, rather naturally, "out fo imself" — individualistic, we might say, focusing on his own personal and material well-being and of course, the welfare of the Joad family. His actions, that is, stem more from particular causes and crises rather than from any sense of general principle as he says, "I put one foot down in front of the other," and "I climb fences when I got to climb fences." He is, however, an admirer and disciple of Jim Casy's almost from the beginning, too, since Jim is the first person from his past whom Tom encounters on his way home from prison. Tom always listens with curiosity and interest to Jim Casy, and later he realizes, as he tells his mother, that he has absorbed more of Casy's philosophizing than he knew. He takes over Jim Casy's philosophy and his tasks at that point after Casy's martyrdom when he quotes the preacher and takes up his credo that "Two are better than one." He speaks in terms of "our people," of doing something so that they may live decently and happily again. Tom Joad has thus enlarged his compassion to all human beings, beyond the family unit.

The women like Ma and Sairy Wilson can of course be included among the ''humanists'' in the novel, for (first of all as mothers) all their actions are outgoing and predominantly selfless. Ma Joad cares about human beings and understands them strikingly well. There are countless examples of her insight and understanding: after Grampa's death, later in the evening, she instructs Rosasharn to go and lie by Granma because ''she'll be feelin' lonesome now''; she is constantly attuned to the complex emotions which come with Rosasharn's pregnancy, compounded by the desertion of her husband Connie — Ma prevents Tom from needling her, yet encourages her to see Tom's jokes about her swelling body as affectionate, which they are; she comprehends that the girl in her loneliness wants to enjoy the Saturday dance at Weedpatch but desperately fears the temptation of her flesh, so that she and Ma go and sit together, Rosasharn secure in Ma's promise to keep her out of trouble; and at the very lowest ebb of her daughter's morale, shortly before her baby is due, Ma makes exactly the right move by giving Rosasharn the gift of gold earrings, one of the few family possessions salvaged, and further distracts her from her troubles by piercing her ears on the spot. Ma silently and without judgment whatsoever acknowledges Uncle John's absolute need to get drunk on the night Jim Casy has stepped forward to go to prison in place of Tom; on another occasion, she breaks down with reasonable and sympathetic words the pathetic defenses of the mother whose hungry children have licked the Joad stew pot and gone home to brag about it. One of the prime instances of Ma's insight into and compassion for humanity is her exchange with the scared little storekeeper at the Hooper ranch, where her hard-earned dollar is so swiftly absorbed by the exorbitant prices set by the Hooper controls. She has complained with perfect justice about the unfair price on each item of her purchases. When finished shopping and on her way out, she realizes that she still has no sugar, which she has promised the family. She asks the man to trust her for the dime's worth of sugar, which her family is earning at the moment out in the orchards. He cannot: company rule. Not even for a dime, Ma asks? ''He looked pleadingly at her. And then his face lost its fear. He took ten cents from his pocket and rang it up in the cash register. 'There,' he said with relief.'' While he cannot go against the owners, out of fear, he can loan money from his own pocket. As Ma gratefully acknowledges his huge gesture, in relative terms, she makes her point about ''humanism'' among the poor people in general: ''I'm learnin' one thing good. Learnin' it all a time, ever' day. If you're in trouble or hurt or need — go to poor people. They're the only ones that'll help — the only ones.''

It might be added that the humanistic philosophy we find in *The Grapes of Wrath* has been attributed to the influence of Transcendental philosophy, which stresses man's worth and dignity and potential depth of character, and to Walt Whitman's exuberant belief in the masses and love of one's fellow man.

Question 5.

What is meant by the application of the term "agrarian philosophy" to *The Grapes of Wrath?*

Answer

Such a philosophy, or thematic strain, which has been linked to what is known as Jeffersonian agrarianism — a form of democracy and a way of life — is everpresent in the novel. That is, Steinbeck elevates farming as a way of life, if it is accompanied by love and respect for the land. For those who love the land and make it a way of life it takes on symbolic meaning: the people identify with cycles of natural growth and contrastingly, when the soil erodes and is worn out it is at the same time the spirit of the people eroding and wearing out. Ideally, then, the land can be a unifying thing, holding people together and bringing serenity and well-being — and importantly, a sense of human dignity. As it is said at one point in the novel, "I am the land, the land is me." But like-wise, if the land is taken away, then a man's identity — and so his self-esteem — is taken away. And if the people are uprooted from the land, then their unity is destroyed, proven in the novel as we witness the disintegration of the Joad family unit. One of the most eloquent pleas for agrarianism comes in an interchapter late in the novel, wherein the spring and the exquisite ripening of all growing things in California is described, then harshly and bitterly contrasted with the wilful destruction of nature's perfections by those who care only to make profit from the orange or the grape — what the author calls the shopkeepers and manufacturers of the land, who have replaced, for profit's sake, the genuine farmers.

Question 6.

How can the word *pragmatism* be related to *The Grapes of Wrath?*

Answer

Pragmatism is generally considered to be one strand of the philosophy found in the novel. As Steinbeck has himself put it, it is also referred to as "non-teleological" or "is" thinking. It means, in brief, looking at things and trying to evaluate them and act upon them as they really *are* instead of as our various preconceived notions or theories tell us they *should* be (hence the distrust of certain conventional "shoulds" of religion in the novel, and their replacement with the realities of human existence and need). Jim Casy, Tom Joad, Ma are all in varying degrees examples of pragmatists: they try to look at life as it really is, without invariably applying standards they have learned somewhere, which are often inapplicable (the many questions about what is or is not "sin" which arise and are resolved through personal reasoning and judgment rather than by preconceived rules illustrate the pragmatic direction of thought in the novel); they are also flexible, noticing the details of one situation which make it different — hence its result or resolution different — from another. At one point, for example, Ma declares that she will take things as they come (when Al has asked her if she is scared about the new life), she will do what she has to do when something happens to require her action: this is exactly the rule of action she adheres to throughout. The shouting religionists say it is a sin to get drunk; yet Uncle John, in his life and deeds one of the kindest men known, sometimes finds it absolutely necessary to his psychic survival to go on a drunk — Ma, as we have seen, does not condemn such an action. Or, for another example, Ma carefully adjusts her behavior in the progress of the Joad family disaster toward Pa, by custom and right the head of the family but by necessity a figure more and more regarded as passive: Ma notes each alteration, judges and acts accordingly. Jim Casy has looked around him, and "listened to the people," as he so often says: and from what he has seen and heard he has had to change his notions of what "sin" is: fleshly pleasure, for instance, especially among people who work hard, assume family responsibilities, help their neighbors, suffer sometimes incredible hardships, he no longer can look upon as sinful. All that is a part of life that must be taken into the consciousness and dealt with; and life is various.

Question 7.
Comment briefly on symbolism in *The Grapes of Wrath*.

Answer
The dust, the turtle, and the grapes can be singled out, and two characters in particular — Jim Casy and Rose of Sharon. The dust symbolizes the erosion of the land and the erosion of the lives of the people. As we see at the beginning of the novel, it has pervaded, discolored, choked and ruined everything. The dust of course is synonymous with "deadness." The land is ruined, a way of life is shattered, and the lives are uprooted. More remotely, the dust also stands for the profiteering owners in the background, who are "dead" — i.e., indifferent — to the life and love of the land, and who are the ultimate cause of the change from fruitful to barren soil. The soil, and the people, have been drained and exploited. We might hazard a guess that the rain at the end of the novel, which is of course excessive, in a way completes the cycle of the dust, which was also excessive. In this way nature has restored a balance and has initiated a new growth cycle. This ties in with other examples of the "rebirth" idea in the ending.

The turtle, which appears and reappears several times early in the novel, stands for survival, for the driving life force in all mankind. For the turtle ploddingly but steadily advances past every obstacle he encounters: the red ant in his path, the truck which tries to crush him, being imprisoned temporarily in Tom Joad's jacket (and he advances, incidentally, toward the southwest, the direction of the mass migration). Also, the turtle is consistently pictured as ancient, lasting, almost primeval: horny head, yellowed toenails, indestructible high dome of a shell, humorous old eyes.

The grapes seem to symbolize both bitterness and plenty (and critics have found Biblical analogies — of both line and situation — for these ambivalent meanings). The title of the novel of course is taken from the song, "Battle Hymn of the Republic," which evokes in image and in feeling an invincible army marching on to victory. And so the Joads and their brothers, in their increasing frustrations and sufferings, are depicted, as an army growing in ever more militant wrath toward an irrevocable demand for restitution and comfort. Grampa, the oldest member of the clan, is the chief spokesman for the grapes as symbols of plenty: all his descriptions of what he is going to do with those luscious grapes out in California vividly suggest largesse, content, freedom.

It has been suggested by critics that the old man (although not so old as Grampa was when he died) who receives sustenance from Rosasharn's breast at the end is a kind of surrogate, or substitute, for Grampa; and since he is saved from starvation, hence from death, this constitutes a rebirth for the Joad clan (Grampa being the actual ''father'') and for the whole people figuratively viewed. In line with this view we have Rosasharn as not only a mother giving nourishment but almost a Christ-figure. There is a passage from Canticles referring to Christ as Rose of Sharon, and suggestive of revitalization; the notion of rebirth through Christ's physical body is of course symbolized in the ritual of communion, also, with the ''bread'' and the ''wine'' which stand for Christ's body and His blood. The clearest figure of the Christ-like prophet, of course, is the philosophizing Jim Casy. His symbolic function can be verified in a number of ways: the initials of his name, of course; his continual soul-searching, culminating in what he himself refers to as his time in the ''wilderness'' when in prison; his life as an example of what he comes to believe; the discipleship of Tom Joad toward him, which he hardly solicits but which Tom seeks in the light of his goodness; the substitution of his own body — symbolically, his life — for Tom's to go to prison, to ''save'' Tom (since for him to go to prison, having broken parole, would be disastrous); and finally, his actual death, which is in essence a martyrdom for the people whom he has lead and comforted and fought for, in which he paraphrases (as he has previously done) the last words of Christ on the cross: ''They don't know what they're doin'.''

Question 8.
Comment briefly on John Steinbeck's style of writing.

Answer
In general, Steinbeck seems to alternate between passages of description (frequently included in short separate chapters called interchapters) and narrative consisting of dialogue and action. The descriptions are often filled with exquisitely observed detail, whether of nature or of the material, man-made world or of human nature. There is a great variety of style in *The Grapes of Wrath*, and it has been attributed to a number of influences, of which the following seem valid: the Bible, particularly the Old Testament (this is substantiated by the fact of the many paraphrases and analogues to the Old Testament in the novel); American poets such as Walt Whitman and Carl Sandburg; John Dos Passos and his so-called ''newsreel technique'' (the chapter treating the used car dealers, for example); the chanting, repetitive

technique of the chorus in Greek tragedy; and of course the folk idiom itself, from which the dialogue is realistically reproduced.

Bibliography

Beach, Joseph Warren. "John Steinbeck: Art and Propaganda." *American Fiction, 1920-1940.* New York: Macmillan, 1942.

Bluestone, George. *"The Grapes of Wrath." Novels Into Film.* Baltimore: Johns Hopkins University Press, 1957.

Boynton, Percy. "John Steinbeck." *America in Contemporary Fiction.* University of Chicago Press, 1940.

Burke, Kenneth. *The Philosophy of Literary Form.* Baton Rouge: Louisiana State University Press, 1941.

Covici, Pascal, Jr. "Work and the Timeliness of *The Grapes of Wrath.*" Lisca, *Grapes.* (Viking Critical Library).

Donohue, Agnes McNeill, ed. *A Casebook on the Grapes of Wrath.* New York: Thomas Y. Crowell Company, 1968.

Donohue, Agnes McNeill, " 'The Endless Journey to No End, Journey and Eden Symbolism in Hawthorne and Steinbeck." Donohue.

Fontenrose, Joseph. *"The Grapes of Wrath." John Steinbeck; An Introduction and Interpretation.* American Authors and Critics Series. New York: Barnes and Noble, 1963. Holt, Rinehart and Winston, 1967.

French, Warren, ed. *A Companion to the Grapes of Wrath.* New York: The Viking Press, 1963.

French, Warren, ed. "The Education of the Heart." *John Steinbeck.* New Haven, Connecticut: College and University Press, 1961.

Frohock, W. M. "John Steinbeck: The Utility of Wrath." *The Novel of Violence in America.* Revised Edition. Dallas: Southern Methodist University Press, 1958.

Geismar, Maxell. "John Steinbeck: Of Wrath and Joy." *Writers in Crisis: The American Novel Between Two Wars.* Boston: Houghton Mifflin, 1942.

Gurko, Leo. "The Joads in California." *The Angry Decade.* New York: Dodd, Mead, 1947.

Hoffman, Frederick J. *The Modern Novel in America, 1900-1950.* Chicago: Henry Regnery, 1951. Gateway Edition, 1956.

Hunter, J. P. "Steinbeck's Wine of Affirmation in *The Grapes of Wrath.*" *Essays in Modern American Literature,* Richard E. Langford, Guy Owen, William Taylor, eds. Deland, Florida: Stetson University Press, 1963.

Lisca, Peter. "The Dynamics of Community in *The Grapes of Wrath.*" *From Irving to Steinbeck: Studies in American Literature,* Motley F. Deakin and Peter Lisca, eds. Gainesville: University of Florida Press, 1972.

Lisca, Peter. "Editor's Introduction: The Pattern of Criticism." *The Grapes of Wrath: Text and Criticism,* The Viking Critical Library Edition. New York: The Viking Press, 1972.

Lisca, Peter. *"The Grapes of Wrath." The Wide World of John Steinbeck.* New Brunswick, New Jersey: Rutgers University Press, 1958.

Lutwack, Leonard. *Heroic Fiction.* Carbondale: Southern Illinois University Press, 1971.

Marks, Lester J. *Thematic Design in the Novels of John Steinbeck.* The Hague: Mouton, 1969.

Miron, George Thomas. *The Truth about John Steinbeck and the Migrants.* Los Angeles: Haynes Corporation, 1939.

Monroe, Elizabeth N. *The Novel and Society.* Chapel Hill: University of North Carolina Press, 1941.

Moore, Harry T. *The Novels of John Steinbeck: A First Critical Study.* Chicago: Normandie House, 1939. Reprinted Port Washington, New York: Kennikat Press, 1968.

Moseley, Edwin M. "Christ as the Brother of Man: Steinbeck's *The Grapes of Wrath." Pseudonyms of Christ in the Modern Novel: Motifs and Methods.* University of Pittsburgh Press, 1963.

Orlova, R. "Money Against Humanity: Notes on the Work of John Steinbeck," trans. Armin Moskovic. Reprinted in French, *Companion.*

Perez, Betty. "House and Home: Thematic Symbols in *The Grapes of Wrath."* Lisca, *Grapes.* (Viking Critical Library).

Pratt, John Clark, *John Steinbeck: A Critical Essay* (pamphlet). Grand Rapids, Michigan: William B. Eerdmans, 1970.

Reed, John R. *"The Grapes of Wrath* and the Esthetics of Indigence." Lisca, *Grapes.* (Viking Critical Library).

Snell, George. *The Shapers of American Fiction: 1798-1947.* New York: Dutton, 1947.

Stovall, Floyd. *American Idealism.* Norman, Oklahoma: University of Oklahoma Press.

Watt, F. W. *John Steinbeck.* Evergreen Pilot Books. New York: Grove Press, 1962.

Rape of the Lock
Wordsworth's Poetry Notes
Works of John Donne
Works of John Dryden
Yeats' Poetry Notes

The Canterbury Tales
The Canterbury Tales
The Knight's Tale
The Pardoner's Tale
Prologue
Wife of Bath's Tale

Chaucer Total Study Editions
Prologue to the Canterbury Tales
Wife of Bath's Tale

Biology
Biology Notes

Chemistry
Elementary Chemistry Notes —
  Revised
How to Solve Chem. Problems
Introduction to Chemistry
Senior Chemistry Notes — Revised

French
Contemporary French Literature
  Notes
French Grammar — Questions and
  Answers
French Grammar Simplified
French Verbs Fully Conjugated
French Verbs Simplified

Geography
Africa, Australia, and South Pacific
  Islands
Asia Notes
Canada and United States
Europe Notes
North and South America
Physical and Human

German
German Grammar Questions and
  Answers
German Grammar Simplified

History
History of Canada
History of Great Britain
History of the United States
Outline of the Age of Renaissance
Outline of the Industrial Revolution in
  Europe
Outline of the Revolutionary Era in
  France

Mathematics
Algebra — Ques. and Ans.
Elementary Algebra Notes
Sec. School Mathematics 1
Sec. School Mathematics 4
Senior Algebra Notes

Philosophy
Philosophy Ques. and Ans.

Physics
Elementary Physics Notes
How to Solve Physics Problems
Senior Physics Notes

Psychology
Introductory Psychology
Psychology Notes
Psychology Ques. and Ans.

Reference
Develop Your Memory Power
Dictionary of Literary Terms
Effective Term Papers and Reports
English Grammar Simplified
Handbook of English Grammar and
  Composition
How to Write Good Essays and
  Critical Reviews
Secrets of Studying English

Sociology
Anthropology — Questions and
  Answers
Sociology

Spanish
Spanish Grammar — Questions and
  Answers